Introduction to the student

This homework book is designed to give you extr[a]
covered in class. Each exercise in *Intermediate M*
(second edition) has a corresponding homework exercise of the same
format in this book.

Very few formulae or worked examples are given in this book. We assume
that these have been provided by your teacher and if you have worked
from the Intermediate book in class, you should have sufficient reference
material in your own notes.

Most exercises include an 'examination-type question' and these are
highlighted with an asterisk ★ in the margin. These questions give you the
opportunity to see how each topic might appear in your examinations.

We wish you every success!

Brian Speed, Keith Gordon and Kevin Evans

July 2001

Mathematics for GCSE (second edition) text books and homework resources have
been written by senior examiners with many years of teaching experience to
provide comprehensive preparation for GCSE Mathematics courses starting from
2001. Though written specifically for AQA specifications A and B, the books are
also suitable for the new Edexcel and OCR qualifications.

Free downloadable resources for teachers
● Comprehensive schemes of work matched to *Mathematics for GCSE* second
   editions
● Revision checklists chapter by chapter

Visit our website for details
www.CollinsEducation.com/Maths

Published by Collins Educational
An imprint of HarperCollins*Publishers* Ltd
77–85 Fulham Palace Road
Hammersmith
London W6 8JB

www.**Collins**Education.com
Online Support for Schools and Colleges

ISBN 0 00 712368 X

British Cataloguing in Publication Data
A catalogue record for this book is available from the British Library

Edited by Simon Gerratt and Benedicta Nakawuki
Typesetting by Derek Lee
Illustrations by Moondisks, Cambridge; Illustrated Arts, Sutton; Barking Dog Art;
    Mark Jordan and Simon Gerratt
Cover by Sylvia Kwan, Chi Leung
Production by Kathryn Botterill
Commissioned by Mark Jordan
Printed and bound by Scotprint, Haddington

You might also like to visit:
www.**fire**and**water**.com
The book lover's website

Chapter 1   Number

HOMEWORK 1A

Calculate the following. Check your answers on a calculator **afterwards**.

1	24×13	**2**	33×17	**3**	54×42	**4**	89×23	**5**	58×53
6	176×14	**7**	235×16	**8**	439×21	**9**	572×35	**10**	678×57

HOMEWORK 1B

Calculate the following. Check your answers on a calculator **afterwards**.

1	$312 \div 13$	**2**	$480 \div 15$	**3**	$697 \div 17$	**4**	$792 \div 22$	**5**	$806 \div 26$
6	$532 \div 28$	**7**	$736 \div 32$	**8**	$595 \div 35$	**9**	$948 \div 41$	**10**	$950 \div 53$

HOMEWORK 1C

Read the problem carefully and then do the calculation to solve the problem.

1   Wall tiles are packed in boxes of 16. Andy buys 24 packs to tile his bathroom. How many tiles does he buy altogether?

2   The organiser of a church fete requires 1000 coloured balloons. How many packets does she need to buy if there are 25 balloons in a packet?

3   A TV rental shop purchases 32 televisions at £112 each.
   a   Find the total cost of the televisions.
   b   Show how you could check your answer by estimation.

4   The annual subscription fee to join a Fishing Club is £42. The treasurer of the club has collected £1134 in fees. How many people have paid their subscription fee?

5   Mrs Woodhead saves £14 per week towards her bills. How much does she save in a year?

6   Sylvia has a part time job and is paid £18 for every day she works. Last year she worked for 148 days. How much was she paid for the year?

7   A coach firm charges £504 for 36 people to go Christmas shopping on a day trip to Calais. How much does each person pay if they share the cost equally between them?

8   A concert hall has 48 rows of seats with 32 seats in a row. What is the maximum capacity of the hall?

★9   Allan is a market gardener and has 420 bulbs to plant. He plants them out in rows with 18 bulbs to a row. How many complete rows will there be?

★10   A room measuring 6 metres by 8 metres is to be carpeted. The carpet costs £19 per square metre.
   a   Estimate the cost of the carpet.
   b   Calculate the exact cost of the carpet.

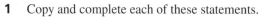
1 Copy and complete each of these statements.

a $\dfrac{1}{5} \to \dfrac{\times 3}{\times 3} = \dfrac{\square}{15}$ **b** $\dfrac{2}{3} \to \dfrac{\times 4}{\times 4} = \dfrac{\square}{12}$ **c** $\dfrac{3}{4} \to \dfrac{\times 2}{\times 2} = \dfrac{\square}{8}$

d $\dfrac{4}{5} \to \dfrac{\times 3}{\times 3} = \dfrac{\square}{\square}$ **e** $\dfrac{1}{4} \to \dfrac{\times 4}{\times 4} = \dfrac{\square}{\square}$ **f** $\dfrac{3}{8} \to \dfrac{\times 5}{\times 5} = \dfrac{\square}{\square}$

g $\dfrac{5}{6} \to \dfrac{\times \square}{\times \square} = \dfrac{20}{\square}$ **h** $\dfrac{7}{10} \to \dfrac{\times \square}{\times \square} = \dfrac{21}{\square}$ **i** $\dfrac{7}{8} \to \dfrac{\times \square}{\times \square} = \dfrac{\square}{40}$

2 Copy and complete each of these statements.

a $\dfrac{3}{5} = \dfrac{6}{\square} = \dfrac{9}{\square} = \dfrac{\square}{25} = \dfrac{\square}{35} = \dfrac{\square}{55}$ **b** $\dfrac{4}{9} = \dfrac{8}{\square} = \dfrac{12}{\square} = \dfrac{\square}{36} = \dfrac{\square}{63} = \dfrac{\square}{81}$

3 Give the answer to each of the following problems in the form of a fraction.

a $2 \div 5$ **b** $3 \div 4$ **c** $3 \div 8$ **d** $2 \div 9$ **e** $9 \div 10$

4 Write down the problem (as above) that would give the following answers.

a $\dfrac{5}{8}$ **b** $\dfrac{2}{5}$ **c** $\dfrac{3}{7}$ **d** $\dfrac{4}{9}$ **e** $\dfrac{7}{10}$

Copy and complete each of these statements.

1   **a** $\dfrac{15}{25} \to \dfrac{\div 5}{\div 5} = \dfrac{\square}{\square}$ **b** $\dfrac{28}{35} \to \dfrac{\div 7}{\div 7} = \dfrac{\square}{5}$ **c** $\dfrac{18}{24} \to \dfrac{\div 6}{\div 6} = \dfrac{\square}{4}$

2 Cancel down each of these fractions.

a $\dfrac{8}{12}$ **b** $\dfrac{4}{10}$ **c** $\dfrac{15}{40}$ **d** $\dfrac{27}{30}$ **e** $\dfrac{35}{49}$ **f** $\dfrac{48}{72}$

3 Which is the larger fraction in each of the following pairs?

a $\dfrac{4}{5}, \dfrac{6}{7}$ **b** $\dfrac{5}{8}, \dfrac{3}{5}$ **c** $\dfrac{3}{4}, \dfrac{5}{9}$ **d** $\dfrac{3}{10}, \dfrac{1}{3}$

4 Put the correct sign, $>$, $=$, $<$ in the box between each of the following pairs.

a $\dfrac{3}{4} \square \dfrac{4}{5}$ **b** $\dfrac{3}{4} \square \dfrac{5}{7}$ **c** $\dfrac{5}{6} \square \dfrac{4}{5}$ **d** $\dfrac{9}{10} \square \dfrac{11}{12}$

e $\dfrac{2}{5} \square \dfrac{1}{3}$ **f** $\dfrac{3}{4} \square \dfrac{5}{8}$ **g** $\dfrac{1}{2} \square \dfrac{3}{5}$ **h** $\dfrac{3}{4} \square \dfrac{2}{3}$

i $\dfrac{3}{5} \square \dfrac{6}{10}$ **j** $\dfrac{1}{4} \square \dfrac{2}{9}$ **k** $\dfrac{2}{5} \square \dfrac{4}{10}$ **l** $\dfrac{5}{6} \square \dfrac{8}{9}$

m $\dfrac{5}{8} \square \dfrac{2}{3}$ **n** $\dfrac{7}{8} \square \dfrac{6}{10}$ **o** $\dfrac{5}{9} \square \dfrac{3}{5}$ **p** $\dfrac{7}{8} \square \dfrac{4}{5}$

1 Calculate these fractions.

a $\frac{4}{5} \times 20$ **b** $\frac{5}{6} \times 18$ **c** $\frac{3}{4} \times 32$ **d** $\frac{3}{10} \times 50$

2 Calculate these fractions.

a $\frac{3}{4}$ of £380   **b** $\frac{2}{3}$ of 114 grams   **c** $\frac{7}{8}$ of 96 kg   **d** $\frac{4}{5}$ of 75p

3 In each case find out which is the smaller number.

a $\frac{3}{5}$ of 70 or $\frac{7}{8}$ of 56   **b** $\frac{2}{3}$ of 87 or $\frac{2}{3}$ of 76

4 A programme seller was entitled to keep $\frac{3}{20}$ of all the sales from the programmes. One match day his sales from the programmes was £115. What was he entitled to keep from the sales?

5 A gardener always insisted on $\frac{3}{8}$ of the garden to be allowed to fallow. If the garden he was tending had an area of $1200\,\text{m}^2$, what area would he want to be fallow?

6 At a Steps concert, there were about 23 000 young people. It was estimated that $\frac{4}{5}$ of these were under 15. How many is this?

7 At an election, the candidates have to gain at least $\frac{2}{15}$ of the vote if they want their deposit back. Alice Crook was standing for election in a constituency where they expected 30 000 voters to cast a vote. What is the smallest number of people that have to vote for her so that she does not lose her deposit?

8 Which is the bigger: seven eighths of sixteen million or four fifths of seventeen million?

9 Which is the smaller: three fifths of two or two fifths of three?

HOMEWORK 1G

You need to do this exercise without a calculator.

1 Change each of these top-heavy fractions into a mixed number.

a $\frac{8}{5}$ b $\frac{5}{3}$ c $\frac{9}{4}$ d $\frac{23}{8}$ e $\frac{13}{2}$ f $\frac{21}{5}$

g $\frac{70}{6}$ h $\frac{17}{8}$ i $\frac{45}{7}$ j $\frac{62}{9}$ k $\frac{71}{10}$ l $\frac{43}{5}$

m $\frac{55}{6}$ n $\frac{29}{5}$ o $\frac{31}{12}$ p $\frac{87}{15}$ q $\frac{53}{4}$ r $\frac{98}{9}$

2 Change each of these mixed numbers into a top-heavy fraction.

a $1\frac{3}{8}$ b $5\frac{2}{3}$ c $4\frac{2}{5}$ d $6\frac{1}{2}$ e $3\frac{3}{4}$ f $9\frac{5}{6}$

g $3\frac{7}{10}$ h $3\frac{5}{8}$ i $12\frac{3}{8}$ j $7\frac{3}{5}$ k $4\frac{3}{4}$ l $7\frac{3}{10}$

m $5\frac{4}{5}$ n $7\frac{3}{8}$ o $2\frac{4}{7}$ p $5\frac{3}{10}$ q $8\frac{5}{8}$ r $3\frac{3}{8}$

HOMEWORK 1H

1 Evaluate the following

a $\frac{1}{2}+\frac{1}{5}$ b $\frac{1}{2}+\frac{1}{3}$ c $\frac{1}{3}+\frac{1}{10}$ d $\frac{3}{8}+\frac{1}{3}$

e $\frac{3}{4}+\frac{1}{5}$ f $\frac{1}{3}+\frac{2}{5}$ g $\frac{3}{5}+\frac{3}{8}$ h $\frac{1}{2}+\frac{2}{5}$

2 Evaluate the following

a $\frac{1}{2}+\frac{1}{4}$ b $\frac{1}{3}+\frac{1}{6}$ c $\frac{3}{5}+\frac{1}{10}$ d $\frac{5}{8}+\frac{1}{4}$

3 Evaluate the following

a $\frac{7}{8}-\frac{3}{4}$ b $\frac{4}{5}-\frac{1}{2}$ c $\frac{2}{3}-\frac{1}{5}$ d $\frac{3}{4}-\frac{2}{5}$

4 Evaluate the following

a $\frac{5}{8}+\frac{3}{4}$ b $\frac{1}{2}+\frac{3}{5}$ c $\frac{5}{6}+\frac{1}{4}$ d $\frac{2}{3}+\frac{3}{4}$

5 At a football club half of the players are English, a quarter are Scottish and one sixth are Italian. The rest are Irish. What fraction of players at the club are Irish?

6 On a firm's coach trip, half the people were employees, two fifths were partners of the employees. The rest were children. What fraction of the people were children?

7 Five eighths of the 35 000 crowd were male. How many females were in the crowd?

8 What is four fifths of sixty-five added to five sixths of fifty-four?

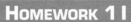 

1 Evaluate the following, leaving your answer in its simplest form.

a $\frac{1}{2} \times \frac{2}{3}$ b $\frac{3}{4} \times \frac{2}{5}$ c $\frac{3}{5} \times \frac{1}{2}$ d $\frac{3}{7} \times \frac{2}{3}$ e $\frac{2}{3} \times \frac{5}{6}$

f $\frac{1}{3} \times \frac{3}{5}$ g $\frac{2}{3} \times \frac{7}{10}$ h $\frac{3}{8} \times \frac{2}{5}$ i $\frac{4}{9} \times \frac{3}{8}$ j $\frac{4}{5} \times \frac{7}{16}$

2 Evaluate the following, leaving your answer as a mixed number where possible.

a $1\frac{1}{3} \times 2\frac{1}{4}$ b $1\frac{3}{4} \times 1\frac{1}{3}$ c $2\frac{1}{2} \times \frac{4}{5}$ d $1\frac{2}{3} \times 1\frac{3}{10}$

e $3\frac{1}{4} \times 1\frac{3}{5}$ f $2\frac{2}{3} \times 1\frac{3}{4}$ g $3\frac{1}{2} \times 1\frac{1}{6}$ h $7\frac{1}{2} \times 1\frac{3}{5}$

3 Kris walked three quarters of the way along Carterknowle Road which is 3 km long. How far did Kris walk?

4 Jean ate one fifth of a cake, Les ate a half of what was left. Nick ate the rest. What fraction of the cake did Nick eat?

5 Billie made a cast that weighed five and three quarter kilograms. Four fifths of this weight is water. What is the weight of the water in Billie's cast?

6 Which is the smaller, $\frac{3}{4}$ of $5\frac{1}{3}$ or $\frac{2}{3}$ of $4\frac{2}{5}$?

7 I bought twenty-four bottles of lemonade, all containing $2\frac{3}{4}$ litres of lemonade. What is the total amount of lemonade I bought?

1 Evaluate the following, leaving your answer as a mixed number where possible.

a $\frac{1}{5} \div \frac{1}{3}$ b $\frac{3}{5} \div \frac{3}{8}$ c $\frac{4}{5} \div \frac{2}{3}$ d $\frac{4}{7} \div \frac{8}{9}$

e $4 \div 1\frac{1}{2}$ f $5 \div 3\frac{2}{3}$ g $8 \div 1\frac{3}{4}$ h $6 \div 1\frac{1}{4}$

i $5\frac{1}{2} \div 1\frac{1}{3}$ j $7\frac{1}{2} \div 2\frac{2}{3}$ k $1\frac{1}{2} \div 1\frac{1}{5}$ l $3\frac{1}{5} \div 3\frac{3}{4}$

2 A pet shop has thirty-six kilograms of hamster food. Tom, who owns the shop, wants to pack this into bags, each containing three quarters of a kilogram. How many bags can he make in this way?

3 Bob is putting a fence down the side of his garden, it is to be 20 metres long. The fence comes in sections; each one is one and one third of a metre long. How many sections will Bob need to put the fence all the way down the one side of his garden?

4 An African Bullfrog can jump a distance of $1\frac{1}{4}$ metres in one hop. How many hops would it take an African Bullfrog to hop a distance of 100 metres?

5 Evaluate the following, leaving your answer as a mixed number wherever possible.

a $\frac{4}{5} \times \frac{1}{2} \times \frac{3}{8}$ b $\frac{3}{4} \times \frac{7}{10} \times \frac{5}{6}$ c $\frac{2}{3} \times \frac{5}{6} \times \frac{9}{10}$

d $1\frac{1}{4} \times \frac{2}{3} \div \frac{5}{6}$ e $\frac{5}{8} \times 1\frac{1}{3} \div 1\frac{1}{10}$ f $2\frac{1}{2} \times 1\frac{1}{3} \div 3\frac{1}{3}$

1 Use a thermometer scale to find the answer to each of the following.

a $3° - 5° =$ b $3° - 6° =$ c $2° - 6° =$ d $2° - 5° =$

e $7° - 9° =$ f $4° - 7° =$ g $-3 + 7 =$ h $-2 + 5 =$

i $-5 + 2 =$ j $-8 + 3 =$ k $-4 + 6 =$ l $-7 + 3 =$

m $-9 - 1 =$ n $-3 - 5 =$ o $-4 - 2 =$ p $5 - 8 =$

q	$3 - 8 =$	r	$2 - 6 =$	s	$-2 + 6 =$	t	$6 - 7 =$
u	$-3 - 4 =$	v	$5 - 8 =$	w	$-7 + 5 =$	x	$5 - 11 =$

2 Answer each of the following without the help of the thermometer scale.

a	$5 - 10 =$	b	$4 - 6 =$	c	$-3 - 7 =$	d	$-4 + 8 =$
e	$-2 + 10 =$	f	$5 - 8 =$	g	$-11 + 17 =$	h	$-13 + 25 =$
i	$22 - 30 =$	j	$40 - 51 =$	k	$-13 + 24 =$	l	$-20 + 56 =$
m	$-10 - 32 =$	n	$-14 - 18 =$	o	$35 - 60 =$	p	$27 - 23 =$
q	$19 - 33 =$	r	$-28 + 37 =$	s	$-33 - 23 =$	t	$35 - 46 =$
u	$-23 + 61 =$	v	$-17 + 32 =$	w	$26 - 66 =$	x	$198 - 400 =$

3 Work out each of the following.

a	$7 + 4 - 6 =$	b	$-3 + 5 - 7 =$	c	$-2 + 6 + 3 =$	d	$-8 - 4 + 7 =$
e	$-2 + 3 - 5 =$	f	$-5 + 7 - 9 =$	g	$-4 + 3 - 8 =$	h	$2 + 4 - 5 =$
i	$9 - 15 + 3 =$						

HOMEWORK 1L

1 Write down the answers to the following.

a	-2×4	b	-3×6	c	-5×7	d	-3×-4	e	-8×-2
f	$-14 \div -2$	g	$-16 \div -4$	h	$25 \div -5$	i	$-16 \div -8$	j	$-8 \div -4$
k	3×-7	l	6×-3	m	7×-4	n	-3×-9	o	-7×-2
p	$28 \div -4$	q	$12 \div -3$	r	$-40 \div 8$	s	$-15 \div -3$	t	$50 \div -2$
u	-3×-8	v	$42 \div -6$	w	7×-9	x	$-24 \div -4$	y	-7×8

2 Write down the answers to the following.

a	$-2 + 4$	b	$-3 + 6$	c	$-5 + 7$	d	$-3 + -4$	e	$-8 + -2$
f	$-14 - -2$	g	$-16 - -4$	h	$25 - -5$	i	$-16 - -8$	j	$-8 - -4$
k	$3 + -7$	l	$6 + -3$	m	$7 + -4$	n	$-3 + -9$	o	$-7 + -2$
p	$28 - -4$	q	$12 - -3$	r	$-40 - 8$	s	$-15 - -3$	t	$50 - -2$
u	$-3 + -8$	v	$42 - -6$	w	$7 + -9$	x	$-24 - -4$	y	$-7 + 8$

3 What number do you multiply -5 by to get the following?

a	25	b	-30	c	50	d	-100	e	75

HOMEWORK 1M

1 Round off each of these numbers to the nearest 10.

a	34	b	67	c	23	d	49	e	55
f	11	g	95	h	123	i	109	j	125

2 Round off each of these numbers to the nearest 100.

a	231	b	389	c	410	d	777	e	850
f	117	g	585	h	250	i	975	j	1245

3 Round off each of these numbers to the nearest 1000.

a	2176	b	3800	c	6760	d	4455	e	1204
f	6782	g	5500	h	8808	i	1500	j	9999

4 Give these bus journey times to the nearest 5 minutes.

a	16 minutes	b	28 minutes	c	34 minutes	d	42 minutes
e	$23\frac{1}{2}$ minutes	f	$17\frac{1}{2}$ minutes				

5 The selling prices of five houses in a village are as follows:

| FOR SALE **£8400** | FOR SALE **£12 900** | FOR SALE **£45 300** | FOR SALE **£75 550** | FOR SALE **£99 500** |

Give the prices to the nearest thousand pounds.

6 Mark knows that he has £240 in his savings account to the nearest ten pounds.
   a What is the smallest amount that he could have?
   b What is the greatest amount that he could have?

7 The size of a crowd at a pop festival was reported to be 8000 to the nearest thousand.
   a What is the lowest number that the crowd could be?
   b What is the largest number that the crowd could be?

HOMEWORK 1N

Examples.   5.852 will round off to 5.85 to two decimal places
                7.156 will round off to 7.16 to two decimal places
                0.284 will round off to 0.3 to one decimal place
                15.3518 will round off to 15.4 to one decimal place

1 Round off each of the following numbers to one decimal place.
   a 3.73   **b** 8.69   **c** 5.34   **d** 18.75   **e** 0.423
   f 26.288   **g** 3.755   **h** 10.056   **i** 11.08   **j** 12.041

2 Round off each of the following numbers to two decimal places.
   a 6.721   **b** 4.457   **c** 1.972   **d** 3.485   **e** 5.807
   f 2.564   **g** 21.799   **h** 12.985   **i** 2.302   **j** 5.555

3 Round off each of the following to the number of decimal places indicated.
   a 0.085 (2 dp)   **b** 4.558 (2 dp)   **c** 2.099 (2 dp)   **d** 0.7629 (3 dp)
   e 7.124 (1 dp)   **f** 8.903 (2 dp)   **g** 23.7809 (3 dp)   **h** 0.99 (1 dp)

4 Round off each of the following to the nearest whole number.
   a 6.7   **b** 9.3   **c** 2.8   **d** 7.5   **e** 8.38
   f 2.82   **g** 2.18   **h** 1.55   **i** 5.252   **j** 3.999

HOMEWORK 1P

1 Round off each of the following numbers to 1 significant figure.
   a 46 313   **b** 57 123   **c** 30 569   **d** 94 558   **e** 85 299
   f 54.26   **g** 85.18   **h** 27.09   **i** 96.432   **j** 167.77
   k 0.5388   **l** 0.2823   **m** 0.005 84   **n** 0.047 85   **o** 0.000 876
   p 9.9   **q** 89.5   **r** 90.78   **s** 199   **t** 999.99

2 What is the least and the greatest number of people that can be found in these towns?
      Hellaby   population 900 (to 1 significant figure)
      Hook   population 650 (to 2 significant figures)
      Hundleton population 1050 (to 3 significant figures)

3 Round off each of the following numbers to 2 significant figures.
   a 6725   **b** 35 724   **c** 68 522   **d** 41 689   **e** 27 308
   f 6973   **g** 2174   **h** 958   **i** 439   **j** 327.6

4 Round off each of the following to the number of significant figures (sf) indicated.

a	46 302 (1 sf)	**b**	6177 (2 sf)	**c**	89.67 (3 sf)	**d**	216.7 (2 sf)
e	7.78 (1 sf)	**f**	1.087 (2 sf)	**g**	729.9 (3 sf)	**h**	5821 (1 sf)
i	66.51 (2 sf)	**j**	5.986 (1 sf)	**k**	7.552 (1 sf)	**l**	9.7454 (3 sf)
m	25.76 (2 sf)	**n**	28.53 (1 sf)	**o**	869.89 (3 sf)	**p**	35.88 (1 sf)
q	0.084 71 (2 sf)	**r**	0.0099 (2 sf)	**s**	0.0809 (1 sf)	**t**	0.061 97 (3 sf)

HOMEWORK 1Q

1 Find approximate answers to the following sums.

a	4324×6.71	**b**	6170×7.311	**c**	72.35×3.142
d	4709×3.81	**e**	$63.1 \times 4.18 \times 8.32$	**f**	$320 \times 6.95 \times 0.98$
g	$454 \div 89.3$	**h**	$26.8 \div 2.97$	**i**	$4964 \div 7.23$
j	$316 \div 3.87$	**k**	$2489 \div 48.58$	**l**	$63.94 \div 8.302$

2 Find the approximate monthly pay of the following people whose annual salary is

    a Joy £47 200   **b** Amy £24 200   **c** Tom £19 135

3 Find the approximate annual pay of these brothers who earn:

    a Trevor £570 a week   **b** Brian £2728 a month

4 A litre of creosote will cover an area of about $6.8 \, m^2$. Approximately how many litre cans will I need to buy to creosote a fence with a total surface area of $43 \, m^2$?

★5 A groundsman bought 350 kg of seed at a cost of £3.84 per kg. Find the approximate total cost of this seed.

6 A greengrocer sells a box of 250 apples for £47. Approximately how much did each apple sell for?

7 Keith runs about 15 km every day. Approximately how far does he run in

    a a week   **b** a month   **c** a year?

HOMEWORK 1R

1 Round off each of the following figures to a suitable degree of accuracy.

    a Kris is 1.6248 metres tall.

    b It took me 17 minutes 48.78 seconds to cook the dinner.

    c My rabbit weighs 2.867 kg.

    d The temperature at the bottom of the ocean is 1.239 °C.

    e There were 23 736 people at the game yesterday.

2 How many jars each holding $119 \, cm^3$ of water can be filled from a 3 litre flask?

3 If I walk at an average speed of 62 metres per minute, how long will it take me to walk a distance of 4 km?

4 Helen earns £31 500 a year. How much does she earn in

    a 1 month   **b** 1 week   **c** 1 day?

5 Dave travelled a distance of 350 miles in 5 hours 40 minutes. What was his average speed?

6 Ten grams of Gold cost £2.17. How much will one kilogram of Gold cost?

 **HOMEWORK 2A**

Example 1   As a fraction $32\% = \frac{32}{100}$ which can be cancelled down to $\frac{8}{25}$

Example 2   As a decimal $65\% = 65 \div 100 = 0.65$

1   Write each percentage as a fraction in its lowest terms.

a 10%	**b** 40%	**c** 25%	**d** 15%	**e** 75%	**f** 35%
g 12%	**h** 28%	**i** 56%	**j** 18%	**k** 42%	**l** 6%

2   Write each percentage as a decimal.

a 87%	**b** 25%	**c** 33%	**d** 5%	**e** 1%	**f** 72%
g 58%	**h** 17.5%	**i** 8.5%	**j** 68.2%	**k** 150%	**l** 132%

3   Copy and complete the table.

Percentage	Fraction	Decimal
10%		
20%		
30%		
		0.4
		0.5
		0.6
	$\frac{7}{10}$	
	$\frac{8}{10}$	
	$\frac{9}{10}$	

4   If 45% of pupils walk to school, what percentage do not walk to school?

5   If 84% of the families in a village own at least one car, what percentage of the families do not own a car?

6   In a local election, of all the people who voted, 48% voted for Mrs Slater, 29% voted for Mr Rhodes and the remainder voted for Mr Mulley. What percentage voted for Mr Mulley?

7   From his gross salary, Mr Hardy pays 20% Income Tax, 6% Superannuation and 5% National Insurance. What percentage is his net pay?

8   Approximately what percentage of each can is filled with oil?

a    **b**    **c**

Example Calculate 12% of 54 kg.

Method 1. $12 \div 100 \times 54 = 6.48$ kg
Method 2. Using the calculator % key.

$$\boxed{5}\ \boxed{4}\ \boxed{\times}\ \boxed{1}\ \boxed{2}\ \boxed{\%}\ \boxed{=}$$

On some calculators you will need to press the $\boxed{=}$ key, while on others you won't.

1 Calculate the following.
  a 25% of £200 **b** 10% of £120 **c** 53% of 400 kg **d** 75% of 84 cm
  e 22% of £84 **f** 71% of 250 g **g** 24% of £3 **h** 95% of 320 m
  i 6% of £42 **j** 17.5% of £56 **k** 8.5% of 160 g **l** 37.2% of £800

2 During one week at a Test Centre, 320 people took their driving test and 65% passed. How many people passed?

3 A school has 250 pupils on roll in each year and the attendance record on one day for each year group was as follows:
Year 7   96%,   Year 8   92%,   Year 9   84%,   Year 10   88%,   Year 11   80%
How many pupils were present in each year group on that day?

4 A certain type of stainless steel consists of 84% iron, 14% chromium and 2% carbon (by weight). How much of each is in 450 tonnes of stainless steel?

★5 Value Added Tax (VAT) is added on to most goods purchased at the rate of $17\frac{1}{2}\%$. How much VAT will be added on to the following bills:
  a a restaurant bill for £40 **b** a telephone bill for £82
  c a car repair bill for £240?

★6 An insurance firm sells house insurance and the annual premiums are usually at a cost of 0.5% of the value of the house. What will be the annual premium for a house valued at £120 000?

Example Increase £6 by 5%.

Method 1. Find 5% of £6: $(5 \div 100) \times 6 = £0.30$
          Add the £0.30 to the original amount: $£6 + £0.30 = £6.30$

Method 2. Using the calculator % key.

$$\boxed{6}\ \boxed{+}\ \boxed{5}\ \boxed{\%}\ \boxed{=}$$

(Again, the $\boxed{=}$ key may not be needed.)

1 Increase each of the following by the given percentage. (Use any method you like.)
  a £80 by 5% **b** £150 by 10% **c** 800 m by 15% **d** 320 kg by 25%
  e £42 by 30% **f** £24 by 65% **g** 120 cm by 18% **h** £32 by 46%
  i 550 g by 85% **j** £72 by 72%

2 Mr Kent, who was on a salary of £32 500, was given a pay rise of 4%. What is his new salary?

3 Copy and complete this electricity bill.

	Total charges
Fixed charges	£13.00
840 units @ 6.45 p per unit	
1720 units @ 2.45 p per unit	
Total charges	
VAT @ 5%	
Total to pay	

4 A bank pays 8% simple interest on the money that each saver keeps in a savings account for a year. Miss Pettica puts £2000 in this account for three years. How much will she have in her account after
   a 1 year   **b** 2 years   **c** 3 years?

 ★5 VAT is a tax that the Government adds to the price of goods sold. At the moment it is 17.5% on all goods. Calculate the price of the following gifts Mrs Dow purchased from a gift catalogue, after VAT of 17.5% has been added.

Gift	Pre-VAT price
Travel alarm clock	£18.00
Ladies' purse wallet	£15.20
Pet's luxury towel	£12.80
Silver-plated bookmark	£6.40

HOMEWORK 2D

1 Decrease each of the following by the given amount.
   a £8 by 4%   **b** 17 kg by 6%   **c** 240 m by 2%

 2 Decrease each of the following by the given amount.
   a 360 g by 10%   **b** 440 m by 15%   **c** 360 cm by 25%

3 A van valued at £8400 last year is now worth 12% less. What is its value now?

 4 A firm employed 80 workers. But it had to streamline its workers and lose 20% of the workers. How many workers does the firm have now?

 5 On the first day of a new term, a school expects to have an attendance rate of 99%. If the school population is 700 pupils, how many pupils will the school expect to be absent on the first day of the new term?

 ★6 Most weighing scales in the home have an error of about 10% from the true reading. When my weighing scales say 500 grams, what is the
   a lowest weight it could represent   **b** largest weight it could represent?

 7 By putting cavity wall insulation into your home, you could use 20% less fuel. A family using an average of 850 units of electricity a year put cavity wall insulation into their home. How much electricity would they expect to use now?

!PROOF 8 Prove that a 10% increase followed by a 10% decrease is equivalent to a 1% decrease overall.

HOMEWORK 2E

1   A small plant increases its height by 10% each day for the second week of its growth. At the end of the first week, the plant was 5 cm high.
What is its height after a further
   a 1 day   **b** 2 days   **c** 4 days   **d** 1 week?

2   The headmaster of a new school offered his staff an annual pay increase of 5% for every year they stayed with the school.
   a Mr Speed started teaching at the school on a salary of £28 000. What salary will he be on after 3 years if he stays at the school?
   b Miss Tuck started teaching at the school on a salary of £14 500. How many years will it be until she is earning a salary of over £20 000?

3   Billy put a gift of £250 into a special savings account that offered him 8% compound interest if he promised to keep the money in for at least 2 years. How much was in this account after
   a 2 years   **b** 3 years   **c** 5 years?

4   The penguin population of a small island was only 1500 in 1998, but it steadily increased by about 15% each year. Calculate the population in
   a 1999   **b** 2000   **c** 2002

 ✭5   A sycamore tree is 40 cm tall, it grows at a rate of 8% per year. A conifer is 20 cm tall. It grows at a rate of 15% per year. How many years does it take before the conifer is taller than the sycamore?

HOMEWORK 2F

Example   Express £6 as a percentage of £40.

Method 1. Set up the fraction $\frac{6}{40}$ and multiply it by 100. $6 \div 40 \times 100\% = 15\%$

Method 2. Using the calculator % key.

     (Again, the ▢ key may not be needed.)

1   Express each of the following as a percentage. Give your answers to 1 decimal place where necessary.
   a £8 of £40   **b** 20 kg of 80 kg   **c** 5 m of 50 m
   d £15 of £20   **e** 400 g of 500 g   **f** 23 cm of 50 cm
   g £12 of £36   **h** 18 minutes of 1 hour   **i** £27 of £40
   j 5 days of 3 weeks

2   What percentage of these shapes is shaded?
   a   **b**

3 In a class of 30 pupils, 18 are girls.
  a What percentage of the class are girls?
  b What percentage of the class are boys?

4 The area of a farm is 820 hectares. The farmer uses 240 hectares for pasture.
What percentage of the farm land is used for pasture? Give your answer to 1 decimal place.

5 Find, to one decimal place, the percentage profit on each of the following.

	Item	Retail price (Selling price)	Wholesale price (Price the shop paid)
a	Micro Hi-Fi System	£250	£150
b	CD Radio Cassette	£90	£60
c	MiniDisc Player	£44.99	£30
d	Cordless Headphones	£29.99	£18

HOMEWORK 2G

1 Find what 100% represents when
  a 20% represents 160 g **b** 25% represents 24 m **c** 5% represents 42 cm

2 Find what 100% represents when
  a 40% represents 28 kg **b** 30% represents £54 **c** 15% represents 6 hours

3 VAT is a government tax added to goods and services. With VAT at 17.5%, what is the pre-VAT price of the following priced goods?
Jumper   £14.10   Socks   £1.88   Trousers   £23.50

4 Paula spends £9 each week on CDs. This is 60% of her weekly income. How much is Paula's weekly income?

5 Alan's weekly pay is increased by 4% to £187.20. What was Alan's pay before the increase?

6 Kev sold his bike for £60, making a profit of 20% on the price he paid for it. How much did Kev pay for the bike?

★7 Gran used 240 g of mixed fruit and nut in a cake. This represented 30% of the weight of the cake. How much did the cake weigh?

8 99 Rock music CDs represents just 18% of my entire CD collection. How many CDs have I?

Chapter 3   Ratio

HOMEWORK 3A

Example 1   Simplify 5 : 20.

$$5 : 20 = 1 : 4 \quad \text{(Divide both sides of the ratio by 5)}$$

Example 2   Simplify 20p : £2.

(Change to a common unit) 20p : 200p = 1:10

Example 3   A garden is divided into lawn and shrubs in the ratio 3 : 2.

The lawn covers $\frac{3}{5}$ of the garden and the shrubs cover $\frac{2}{5}$ of the garden.

1   Express each of the following ratios in their simplest form.
- **a**   3 : 9
- **b**   5 : 25
- **c**   4 : 24
- **d**   10 : 30
- **e**   6 : 9
- **f**   12 : 20
- **g**   25 : 40
- **h**   30 : 4
- **i**   14 : 35
- **j**   125 : 50

2   Express each of the following ratios of quantities in their simplest form. (Remember to change to a common unit where necessary.)
- **a**   £2 to £8
- **b**   £12 to £16
- **c**   25 g to 200 g
- **d**   6 miles : 15 miles
- **e**   20 cm : 50 cm
- **f**   80p : £1.50
- **g**   1 kg : 300 g
- **h**   40 seconds : 2 minutes
- **i**   9 hours : 1 day
- **j**   4 mm : 2 cm

3   £20 is shared out between Bob and Kathryn in the ratio 1 : 3.
- **a**   What fraction of the £20 does Bob receive?
- **b**   What fraction of the £20 does Kathryn receive?

4   In a class of students, the ratio of boys to girls is 2 : 3.
- **a**   What fraction of the class is boys?
- **b**   What fraction of the class is girls?

5   Pewter is an alloy containing lead and tin in the ratio 1 : 9.
- **a**   What fraction of pewter is lead?
- **b**   What fraction of pewter is tin?

 HOMEWORK 3B

Example   Divide £40 between Peter and Hitan in the ratio 2 : 3.

Changing the ratio to fractions gives
Peter's share = $\frac{2}{5}$ and Hitan's share = $\frac{3}{5}$
So, Peter receives $\frac{2}{5} \times £40 = £16$ and Hitan receives $\frac{3}{5} \times £40 = £24$

 1   Divide each of the following amounts in the given ratios.
- **a**   £10 in the ratio 1 : 4
- **b**   £12 in the ratio 1 : 2
- **c**   £40 in the ratio 1 : 3
- **d**   60 g in the ratio 1 : 5
- **e**   10 hours in the ratio 1 : 9
- **f**   25 kg in the ratio 2 : 3
- **g**   30 days the ratio 3 : 2
- **h**   70 m in the ratio 3 : 4
- **i**   £5 in the ratio 3 : 7
- **j**   1 day in the ratio 5 : 3

 2   The ratio of female to male members of a Sports Centre is 3 : 1. The total number of members of the Centre is 400.
- **a**   How many members are female?
- **b**   How many members are male?

3   A 20 metre length of cloth is cut into two pieces in the ratio 1 : 9. How long is each piece?

4   James collects beer mats and the ratio of British mats to foreign mats is 5 : 2. He has 1400 beer mats in his collection. How many foreign beer mats does he have?

5   Patrick and Jane share out a box of sweets in the ratio of their ages. Patrick is 9 years old and Jane is 11 years old. If there are 100 sweets in the box, how many does Patrick get?

★6 For her birthday Reena is given £30. She decides to spend four times as much as she saves. How much does she save?

7 Mrs Megson calculates that her quarterly electricity and gas bills are in the ratio 5 : 6. The total she pays for both bills is £66. How much is each bill?

8 You can simplify a ratio by changing it into the form 1 : *n*. For example, 5 : 7 can be rewritten as 5 : 7 = 1 : 1.4 by dividing each side of the ratio by 5. Rewrite each of the following ratios in the form 1 : *n*.

   a   2 : 3   **b**   2 : 5   **c**   4 : 5   **d**   5 : 8   **e**   10 : 21

 HOMEWORK 3C

Example   Two business partners, John and Ben, divided their total profit in the ratio 3 : 5. John received £2100. How much did Ben get?

John's £2100 was $\frac{3}{8}$ of the total profit.

So, $\frac{1}{8}$ of the total profit = £2100 ÷ 3 = £700.

Therefore, Ben's share, which was $\frac{5}{8}$, amounted to £700 × 5 = £3500.

1 Peter and Margaret's ages are in the ratio 4 : 5. If Peter is 16 years old, how old is Margaret?

2 Cans of lemonade and packets of crisps were bought for the school disco in the ratio 3 : 2. The organiser bought 120 cans of lemonade. How many packets of crisps did she buy?

3 In his restaurant, Manuel is making 'Sangria', a drink made from red wine and iced soda water, mixed in the ratio 2 : 3. Manuel uses 10 litres of red wine.

   a   How many litres of soda water does he use?

   b   How many litres of Sangria does he make?

4 Cupro-nickel coins are minted by mixing copper and nickel in the ratio 4 : 1.

   a   How much copper is needed to mix with 20 kg of nickel?

   b   How much nickel is needed to mix with 20 kg of copper?

 5 The ratio of male to female spectators at a school inter-form football match is 2 : 1. If 60 boys watched the game, how many spectators were there in total?

 ★6 Marmalade is made from sugar and oranges in the ratio 3 : 5. A jar of 'Savilles' marmalade contains 120 g of sugar.

   a   How many grams of oranges are in the jar?

   b   How many grams of marmalade are in the jar?

 ★7 Each year Abbey School holds a sponsored walk for charity. The money raised is shared between a local charity and a national charity in the ratio 1 : 2. Last year the school gave £2000 to the local charity.

   a   How much did the school give to the national charity?

   b   How much did the school raise in total?

 HOMEWORK 3D

The relationship between speed, time and distance can be expressed in three ways:

$$\text{Distance} = \text{Speed} \times \text{Time} \qquad \text{Speed} = \frac{\text{Distance}}{\text{Time}} \qquad \text{Time} = \frac{\text{Distance}}{\text{Speed}}$$

Example   Sean is going to drive from Newcastle upon Tyne to Nottingham, a distance of 190 miles. He estimates that he will drive at an average speed of 50 mph. How long will it take him?

Sean's time = $\frac{190}{50}$ = 3.8 hours

Change the 0.8 hours to minutes by multiplying by 60, to give 48 minutes. So, the time for Sean's journey will be 3 hours 48 minutes.

Remember   When you calculate a time and get a decimal answer, do not mistake the decimal part for minutes. You must either

● leave the time as a decimal number and give the unit as hours, or
● change the decimal part to minutes by multiplying it by 60 (1 hour = 60 minutes) and give the answer in hours and minutes.

1   A cyclist travels a distance of 60 miles in 4 hours. What was her average speed?

2   How far along a motorway will you travel if you drive at an average speed of 60 mph for 3 hours?

3   Mr Baylis drives on a business trip from Manchester to London in $4\frac{1}{2}$ hours. The distance he travels is 207 miles. What is his average speed?

4   The distance from Leeds to Birmingham is 125 miles. The train I catch travels at an average speed of 50 mph. If I catch the 11.30 am train in Leeds, at what time would I expect to be in Birmingham?

5   Copy and complete the following table.

	Distance travelled	Time taken	Average speed
a	240 miles	8 hours	
b	150 km	3 hours	
c		4 hours	5 mph
d		$2\frac{1}{2}$ hours	20 km/h
e	1300 miles		400 mph
f	90 km		25 km/h

★**6**   A coach travels at an average speed of 60 km/h for 2 hours on a motorway and then slows down in a town centre to do the last 30 minutes of a journey at an average speed of 20 km/h.
    a   What is the total distance of this journey?
    b   What is the average speed of the coach over the whole journey?

★**7**   Hilary cycles to work each day. She cycles the first 5 miles at an average speed of 15 mph and then cycles the last mile in 10 minutes.
    a   How long does it take her to get to work?
    b   What is her average speed for the whole journey?

★**8**   Martha drives home from work in 1 hour 15 minutes. She drives home at an average speed of 36 mph.
    a   Change 1 hour 15 minutes to decimal time in hours.
    b   How far is it from Martha's work to her home?

1   Find the density of a piece of wood weighing 135 g and having a volume of 150 cm³.

2   Calculate the density of a metal if 40 cm³ of it weighs 2500 g.

3   Calculate the weight of a piece of plastic, 25 cm³ in volume, if its density is 1.2 g/cm³.

4   Calculate the volume of a piece of wood which weighs 350 g and has a density of 0.9 g/cm³.

5   Find the weight of a marble statue, 540 cm³ in volume, if the density of marble is 2.5 g/cm³.

6   Calculate the volume of a liquid weighing 1 kg and having a density of 1.1 g/cm³.

7   Find the density of the material of a stone which weighs 63 g and has a volume of 12 cm³.

8   It is estimated that a huge rock balanced in the ceiling of a cave has a volume of 120 m³. The density of the rock is 8.3 g/cm³. What is the estimated weight of the rock?

9   A 1 kg bag of flour has a volume of about 900 cm³. What is the density of flour in g/cm³?

Chapter 4   Shape

HOMEWORK 4A

1   Copy and complete the following table for rectangles **a** to **c**.

	Length	Breadth	Perimeter	Area
a	8 cm	5 cm		
b	10 cm		36 cm	
c	9 cm			27 cm²

2   Find the total perimeter and the total area of each of these shapes.

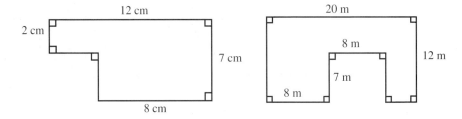

3   Bill, the groundsman, is marking out a hockey pitch. He marks out a rectangle 60 metres long and 30 metres wide.
    a   What is the perimeter of this hockey pitch?
    b   What is the area of this hockey pitch?

4   What is the perimeter of a square with an area of 49 cm²?

5   Ian is painting a large blank wall, 40 metres wide and 12 metres high, with whitewash. Whitewash will cover the wall at a rate of 4.2 square metres per litre. How much paint would you expect Ian to use in painting this wall?

HOMEWORK 4B

1 Find the circumference of each of the following circles. Round off your answers to 1 dp.

    a   Diameter 3 cm   **b**   Radius 5 cm   **c**   Radius 8 m

    d   Diameter 14 cm   **e**   Diameter 6.4 cm   **f**   Radius 3.5 cm

2 John runs twice round a circular track which has a radius of 50 m. How far has he run? Give your answers in terms of π.

3 A rolling pin has a diameter of 5 cm.

    a   What is the circumference of the rolling pin?

    b   How many revolutions does it make when rolling a length of 30 cm?

4 What is the total perimeter of a semicircle of diameter 7 cm? Give your answer to 1 dp.

5 What is the total perimeter of a semicircle of radius 6 cm? Give your answer in terms of π.

6 How many complete revolutions will a bicycle wheel, radius 28 cm, make in a journey of 3 km?

★7 A circle has a circumference of 12 cm. What is its diameter?

HOMEWORK 4C

1 Write down the area and the perimeter of each triangle.

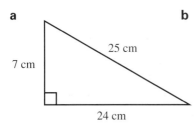 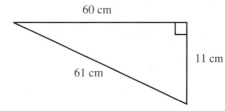

2 Find the area of the shaded part of each triangle.

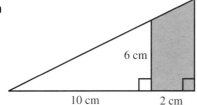 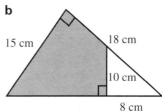

3 Calculate the area of each of these shapes.

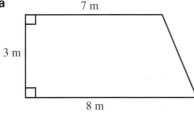 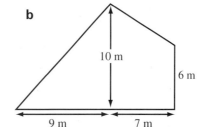

4 A right-angled triangle has an area of 60 cm² and is 12 cm high. What is the base length of the triangle?

1 Copy and complete the following table for triangles **a** to **c**.

	Base	Vertical height	Area
a	10 cm	7 cm	
b	8 cm		24 cm²
c		9 cm	36 cm²

2 Find the area of these shapes.

a

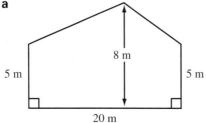

b

3 Find the area of the shaded shape.

a

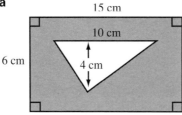

b

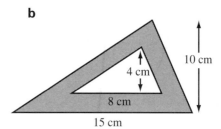

4 Write down the dimensions of five different sized triangles that have the same area of 60 cm².

5 Write down the dimensions of six different sized triangles that have the area of 100 cm².

6 I have a triangle of area 32 cm². The triangle is isosceles, it has two sides of the same length. The lengths of the triangle are all whole numbers of centimetres. What is the missing dimension of the triangle?

1 Calculate the perimeter and the area of each of these trapeziums.

a

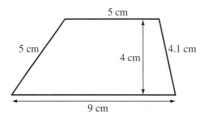

b

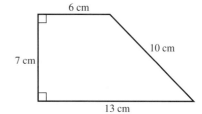

2 Calculate the area of each of these shapes.

a

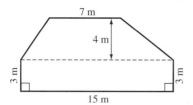

b

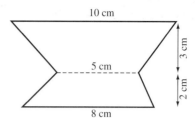

 3 Calculate the area of the shaded part in each of these diagrams.

a

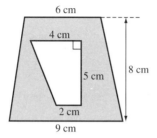

b

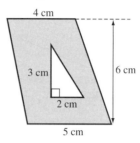

4 Which of the following shapes has the largest area?

a

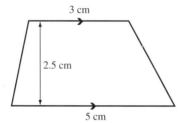

b

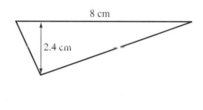

5 What percentage of this shape has been shaded?

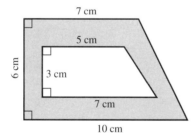

 HOMEWORK 4F

1 Calculate the area of each of these circles, giving your answers to 1 decimal place, except for **a** and **d**, where your answer should be in terms of π.

   a   Radius 4 cm   **b**   Diameter 14 cm   **c**   Radius 9 cm

   d   Diameter 2 m   **e**   Radius 21 cm   **f**   Diameter 0.9 cm

2 A garden has a circular lawn of diameter 20 m. There is a path 1 m wide all the way round the circumference. What is the area of this path?

3 Calculate the area of a semi-circle with a diameter of 15 cm. Give your answer to 1 dp.

4   A circle has an area of 50 m². What is its radius?

★5   I have a circle with a circumference of 25 cm. What is the area of this circle?
Give your answer to 1 decimal place.

 6   Jane walked around a circular lawn. She counted 153 paces to walk round it. Each of her
paces was about 42 cm. What is the area of the lawn?

HOMEWORK 4G

Leave all your answers in terms of π

1   State the circumference of the following circles.
  a   Diameter 7 cm   **b**   Radius 5 cm   **c**   Diameter 19 cm   **d**   Radius 3 cm

2   State the area of the following circles
  a   Radius 8 cm   **b**   Diameter 7 cm   **c**   Diameter 18 cm   **d**   Radius 9 cm

3   State the diameter of a circle with a circumference of 4π cm.

4   State the radius of a circle with an area of 25π cm².

5   State the diameter of a circle with a circumference of 20 cm.

6   State the radius of a circle with an area of 20 cm².

7   What are the radii of the circles with the same area as the following squares?
  a   Side length 12 cm   **b**   Side length 7 cm   **c**   Side length 1.44 cm²

Chapter 5   Volume and surface area

HOMEWORK 5A

Example   Calculate the volume and surface area of
this cuboid.

$$\text{Volume} = 6 \times 4 \times 3.5 = 84 \text{ cm}^3$$
$$\text{Surface area} = (2 \times 6 \times 4) + (2 \times 3.5 \times 4) +$$
$$(2 \times 3.5 \times 6)$$
$$= 48 + 28 + 42 = 118 \text{ cm}^2$$

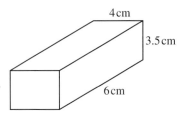

1   Find **i** the volume and **ii** the surface area of each of these cuboids.
  a

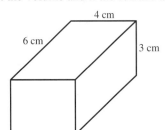

  b

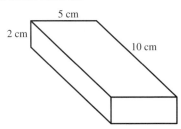

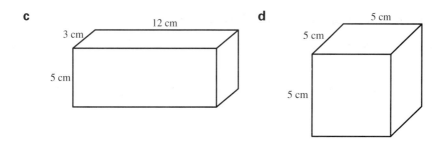

c 12 cm 3 cm 5 cm

d 5 cm 5 cm 5 cm

2 Copy and complete the table which shows the dimensions and volumes of four cuboids.

Length	Width	Height	Volume
4 cm	3 cm	2 cm	24 cm²
5	3 cm	3 cm	45 cm³
8 cm	5	4 cm	160 cm³
6 cm	6 cm	6	216 cm³

3 Find the capacity (volume of a liquid or a gas) of a swimming pool whose dimensions are: length 12 m, width 5 m and depth 1.5 m.

4 Find the volume of the cuboid in each of the following cases.
 a The area of the base is 20 cm² and the height is 3 cm.
 b The base has one side 4 cm, the other side 1 cm longer, and the height is 8 cm.
 c The area of the top is 40 cm² and the depth is 3 cm.

★5 How many 'stock-cubes' will fit into the box?

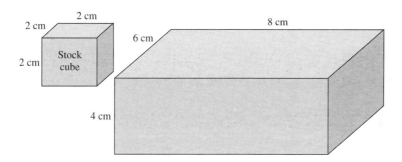

2 cm 2 cm 2 cm Stock cube 6 cm 8 cm 4 cm

6 Calculate the volume of each of these shapes.

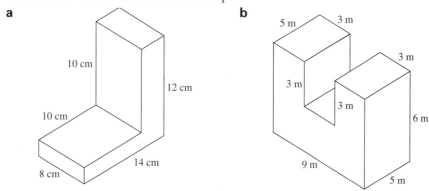

 a 10 cm 12 cm 10 cm 8 cm 14 cm

 b 5 m 3 m 3 m 3 m 3 m 6 m 9 m 5 m

27/1/04

1 Calculate the volume of each of these cylinders.
  a Base radius 5 cm and a height of 7 cm.
  b Base radius 10 cm and a height of 8 cm.
  c Base diameter of 12 cm and a height of 20 cm.
  d Base diameter of 9 cm and a height of 9 cm.

2 Find the volume of each of these cylinders.

 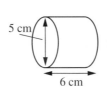 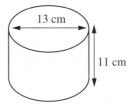

3 What is the weight of a solid iron bar 40 cm long with a radius of 2 cm? The density of iron is 8 grams per cm^3.

4 What is the radius of a cylinder 10 cm long with a volume of 300 cm^3?

5 A drainage pipe has an outer diameter of 100 cm with the outside 4 cm thick. The pipe is 4 metres long and made of hard plastic with a density of 2.6 g/cm^3. What will be the total weight of 50 such drainage pipes?

6 A solid iron cylinder of radius 5 cm and length 25 cm is melted down to make wire 0.02 cm thick (diameter). What length of wire is made?

7 Give the answers to this question in terms of π.
  a What is the volume of a cylinder with a radius of 4 cm and a height of 11 cm?
  b What is the volume of a cylinder with a diameter of 16 cm and a height of 18 cm?

1 For each prism shown, calculate the area of the cross-section and the volume.
  a   **b**

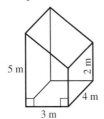 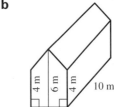

2 Which of these solids is
a the heaviest **b** the lightest?

i (1.26 g/cm³)
12 cm
4 cm

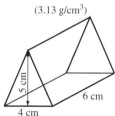
ii (3.13 g/cm³)
5 cm
4 cm
6 cm

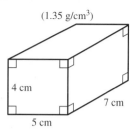
iii (1.35 g/cm³)
4 cm
5 cm
7 cm

Chapter 6   Algebra 1

HOMEWORK 6A

1 Write down the algebraic expression that says
   a 4 more than x **b** 7 less than x **c** k more than 3
   d t less than 8   **e** x added to y **f** x multiplied by 4
   g 5 multiplied by t **h** a multiplied by b **i** m divided by 2
   j p divided by q

2 Write each of these expressions in a shorter form.
   a $a + a + a$ **b** $3b + 2b$ **c** $3c + c + 5c$ **d** $5d - d$
   e $5e + 2e - 4e$ **f** $7f - 2f + 3f$ **g** $2g + 4g - 6g$ **h** $4h - 6h$
   i $3i^2 + 2i^2$ **j** $5j^2 + j^2 - 2j^2$

3 Simplify each of the following expressions.
   a $2y + 5x + y + 3x$ **b** $4m + 6p - 2m + 4p$ **c** $3x + 6 + 3x - 2$
   d $7 - 5x - 2 + 8x$ **e** $5p + 2t + 3p - 2t$ **f** $4 + 2x + 4x - 6$
   g $4p - 4 - 2p - 2$ **h** $4x + 3y + 2x - 5y$ **i** $4 + 3t + p - 6t + 3 + 5p$
   j $4w - 3k - 2w - k + 4w$

4 Multiply out each of the following brackets.
   a $2(a + 4)$ **b** $3(b - 3)$ **c** $5(c + 1)$ **d** $2(2e + 5)$
   e $4(3e - 1)$ **f** $5(5m + 7)$ **g** $2(5a + 2b)$ **h** $2(3x - 4y)$
   i $3(4p + q)$ **j** $a(a + 3)$ **k** $b(b - 2)$ **l** $x(2x + 5)$

5 Val is x years old. Dave is four years older than Val and Ella is five years younger than Val.
   a How old is Dave?   **b** How old is Ella?

6 A packet contains n sweets.

The total number of sweets here is $2n + 3$.
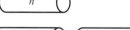

Write down an expression for the total number of sweets in the following.
a

b
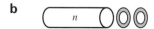

c
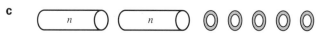

7   Sue has p pets.
- Frank has two more pets than Sue.
- Chloe has three less pets than Sue.
- Lizzie has twice as many pets as Sue.

How many pets does each person have?

8   **a**   Tom has £20 and spends £16. How much does he have left?

    b   Sam has £10 and spends £a. How much does he have left?

    c   Ian has £b and spends £c. How much does he have left?

9   **a**   How many days are there in 3 weeks?

    b   How many days are there in z weeks?

★10   **a**   Granny Parker divides £30 equally between her 3 grandchildren. How much does each receive?

    b   Granny Smith divides £r equally between her 4 grandchildren. How much does each receive?

    c   Granny Thomas divides £p equally between her q grandchildren. How much does each receive?

HOMEWORK 6B

Example   The expression $3x + 2$ has the value 5 when $x = 1$ and 14 when $x = 4$.

1   Find the value of $2x + 3$ when

    a $x = 2$ **b** $x = 5$ **c** $x = 10$

2   Find the value of $3k - 4$ when

    a $k = 2$ **b** $k = 6$ **c** $k = 12$

3   Find the value of $4 + t$ when

    a $t = 4$ **b** $t = 20$ **c** $t = \frac{1}{2}$

4   Evaluate $10 - 2x$ when

    a $x = 3$ **b** $x = 5$ **c** $x = 6$

5   Evaluate $5y + 10$ when

    a $y = 5$ **b** $y = 10$ **c** $y = 15$

6   Evaluate $6d - 2$ when

    a $d = 2$ **b** $d = 5$ **c** $d = \frac{1}{2}$

7   Find the value of $\dfrac{x + 2}{4}$ when

    a $x = 6$ **b** $x = 10$ **c** $x = 18$

8   Find the value of $\dfrac{3x - 1}{2}$ when

    a $x = 1$ **b** $x = 3$ **c** $x = 4$

9   Evaluate $\dfrac{20}{p}$ when

    a $p = 2$ **b** $p = 10$ **c** $p = 20$

10   Find the value of $3(2y + 5)$ when

    a $y = 1$ **b** $y = 3$ **c** $y = 5$

HOMEWORK 6C

1 Where $P = x^2$, find P when   **a** $x = 4$ **b** $x = -4$ **c** $x = 1.1$

 2 Where $H = a^2 + c^2$, find H when   **a** $a = 3$ and $c = 4$ **b** $a = 5$ and $c = 12$

3 Where $K = m^2 - n^2$, find K when   **a** $m = 5$ and $n = 3$ **b** $m = -5$ and $n = -2$

4 Where $P = 100 - n^2$, find P when   **a** $n = 7$ **b** $n = 8$ **c** $n = 9$

5 Where $D = 5x - y$, find D when   **a** $x = 4$ and $y = 3$ **b** $x = 5$ and $y = -3$

6 Where $t = 50 - w$, find t when   **a** $w = 64$ **b** $w = 25$ **c** $w = 100$

Give the answers to the following.

7 Where $T = y(2x + 3y)$, find T when   **a** $x = 8$ and $y = 12$ **b** $x = 5$ and $y = 7$

8 Where $m = w(t^2 + w^2)$, find m when   **a** $t = 5$ and $w = 3$ **b** $t = 8$ and $w = 7$

HOMEWORK 6D

Solve the following equations.

Give your answers as fractions or decimals as appropriate.

1 $5x + 4 = 13$	**2** $4x - 11 = 23$	**3** $2x - 5 = 28$	**4** $3y - 17 = 6$
5 $4a + 9 = 12$	**6** $3x + 7 = 17$	**7** $7 + 3y = 19$	**8** $9x + 5 = 13$
9 $3x - 12 = 7$	**10** $7x + 7 = 67$	**11** $2y - 8 = 5$	**12** $5x - 6 = 16$
13 $3y + 5 = 18$	**14** $9 + 4t = 12$	**15** $3 + 3f = 11$	**16** $5 + 7k = 21$
17 $5x + 8 = 15$	**18** $4m - 7 = 12$	**19** $2t - 19 = 28$	**20** $9d + 8 = 13$
21 $3x + 7 = 11$	**22** $5y - 2 = 7$	**23** $3p + 5 = 11$	**24** $6t - 5 = 4$

HOMEWORK 6E

Solve the following equations.

1 $\dfrac{m}{3} = 4$ **2** $\dfrac{k}{4} = 3$ **3** $\dfrac{w}{5} = 7$ **4** $\dfrac{x}{3} = 8$

5 $\dfrac{h}{7} = 5$ **6** $\dfrac{d}{5} = 4$ **7** $\dfrac{p}{2} + 5 = 7$ **8** $\dfrac{k}{4} - 3 = 5$

9 $\dfrac{g}{3} + 2 = 8$ **10** $\dfrac{m}{4} - 5 = 2$ **11** $\dfrac{f}{6} + 3 = 12$ **12** $\dfrac{h}{8} - 3 = 5$

13 $\dfrac{2h}{3} + 3 = 7$ **14** $\dfrac{5t}{4} - 2 = 6$ **15** $\dfrac{4d}{5} + 3 = 18$ **16** $\dfrac{3x}{4} - 1 = 8$

17 $\dfrac{5w}{3} + 5 = 12$ **18** $\dfrac{3m}{4} - 3 = 7$ **19** $\dfrac{8d}{7} + 3 = 2$ **20** $\dfrac{5g}{8} + 4 = 3$

HOMEWORK 6F

Solve the following equations.

1 $4x + 9 = 7$ **2** $5t + 6 = 2$ **3** $12 + 4x = 5$ **4** $14 + 2y = 3$

5 $7 - 5x = 11$ **6** $8 - 8t = 19$ **7** $7 - 4x = 22$ **8** $5x + 7 = 5$

9 $\dfrac{x+5}{3}=2$ **10** $\dfrac{t+12}{2}=5$ **11** $\dfrac{w-3}{5}=3$ **12** $\dfrac{y-9}{2}=3$

13 $\dfrac{2x-1}{3}=5$ **14** $\dfrac{5t+9}{2}=3$ **15** $\dfrac{4m+2}{5}=5$ **16** $\dfrac{8p-7}{5}=2$

17 $\dfrac{5x+19}{4}=4$ **18** $\dfrac{17+2t}{9}=1$ **19** $\dfrac{23+4x}{3}=4$ **20** $\dfrac{8-2x}{11}=1$

HOMEWORK 6G

Solve the following equations. Give your answers as fractions or decimals as appropriate.

1 $3(x+6)=15$ **2** $6(x-5)=30$ **3** $4(t+3)=20$

4 $5(4x+3)=45$ **5** $3(5y-7)=15$ **6** $4(5x+2)=70$

7 $3(4t-1)=78$ **8** $3(4t+5)=51$ **9** $4(6x+5)=10$

10 $5(4y-1)=47$ **11** $5(2k+3)=36$ **12** $5(3x+8)=30$

13 $3(5y-7)=21$ **14** $3(6t-5)=57$ **15** $8(2x-7)=60$

16 $8(3x-4)=12$ **17** $4(x+7)=7$ **18** $3(x-5)=-24$

19 $5(t+3)=12$ **20** $4(3x-13)=7$ **21** $5(4t+3)=17$

22 $2(5x-3)=-31$ **23** $4(6y-7)=-5$ **24** $3(2x+7)=9$

HOMEWORK 6H

1 Without using a calculator, find the two consecutive whole numbers between which the solution to each of the following equations lies.

   a $x^3=10$ **b** $x^3=50$ **c** $x^3=800$ **d** $x^3=300$

 2 Find a solution to each of the following equations to 1 decimal place. Do not use the cube root on your calculator.

   a $x^3=24$ **b** $x^3=100$ **c** $x^3=500$ **d** $x^3=200$

3 Find two consecutive whole numbers between which the solution to each of the following equations lies.

   a $x^3+x=7$ **b** $x^3+x=55$ **c** $x^3+x=102$ **d** $x^3+x=89$

4 Find a solution to each of the following equations to 1 decimal place.

   a $x^3-x=30$ **b** $x^3-x=95$ **c** $x^3-x=150$ **d** $x^3-x=333$

5 Show that $x^3+x=45$ has a solution between $x=3$ and $x=4$, and find the solution to 1 decimal place.

6 Show that $x^3-2x=95$ has a solution between $x=4$ and $x=5$, and find the solution to 1 decimal place.

HOMEWORK 6 I

1 A rectangle has an area of $200\,\text{cm}^2$. Its length is 8 cm longer than its width. Find, correct to 1 decimal place, the dimensions of the rectangle.

2 A gardener wants his rectangular lawn to be 15 m longer than the width, and the area of the lawn to be $800\,\text{m}^2$. What are the dimensions he should make his lawn? (Give your solution to 1 decimal place.)

3 A triangle has a vertical height 2 cm longer than its base length. Its area is 20 cm². What are the dimensions of the triangle? (Give your solution to 1 decimal place.)

4 A rectangular picture has a height 3 cm shorter than its length. Its area is 120 cm². What are the dimensions of the picture? (Give your solution to 1 decimal place.)

5 What are the dimensions, to 1 decimal place, of a cube that has a volume of 500 cm³?

6 What is the length of one side of a cube with volume 44 m³? (Give your answer to 1 decimal place.)

7 Find, correct to 1 decimal place, the solution to $x^4 = 64$.

Chapter 7   Geometry

 HOMEWORK 7A

1 Use a protractor to find the size of each marked angle.

a  **b**

c **d**

e **f**

g  **h**

2 Draw angles of the following sizes.
    a 30°   **b** 42°   **c** 55°   **d** 68°   **e** 75°   **f** 140°
    g 164°   **h** 245°

3 **a** Draw any three acute angles.
    b Estimate their sizes. Record your results.
    c Measure the angles. Record your results.
    d Work out the difference between your estimate and your measurement for each angle.

1 Calculate the value of *x* in each of these situations.

a

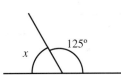

b

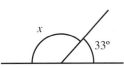

c

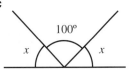

2 Calculate the values of *x* and *y* in each of these situations.

a

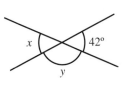

b

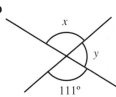

c

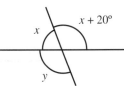

3 Calculate the value of *x* in each of these triangles.

a   **b**

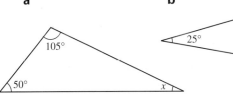

c

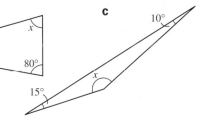

4 Calculate the value of *x* in each of these situations.

a

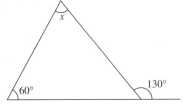

b

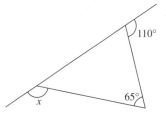

1 State the size of the lettered angles in each diagram.

a

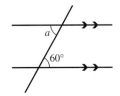

b

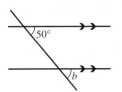

c

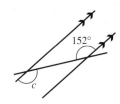

d

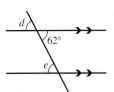

e

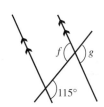

f

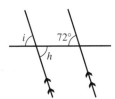

2 State the size of the lettered angles in each diagram.

a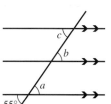

b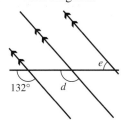

c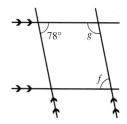

3 State the size of the lettered angles in these diagrams.

a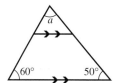

b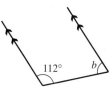

HOMEWORK 7D

1 Calculate the sum of the interior angles of polygons with
  a 7 sides   **b** 11 sides   **c** 20 sides   **d** 35 sides

2 Calculate the size of the interior angle of regular polygons with
  a 15 sides   **b** 18 sides   **c** 30 sides   **d** 100 sides

3 Find the number of sides of the polygon with the interior angle sum of
  a 1440°   **b** 2520°   **c** 6120°   **d** 6840°

 4 Find the number of sides of the regular polygon with an exterior angle of
  a 20°   **b** 30°   **c** 18°   **d** 4°

 5 Find the number of sides of the regular polygon with an interior angle of
  a 135°   **b** 165°   **c** 170°   **d** 156°

 6 What is the name of the regular polygon whose interior angle is treble its exterior angle?

 ★7 Anne measured all the interior angles in a polygon. She added them up to make 1325°, but she had missed out one angle. What is the
  a name of the polygon that Anne measured
  b size of the missing angle?

HOMEWORK 7E

1 Calculate the lettered angles in each triangle.

a   **b**   **c** 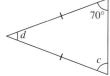   **d**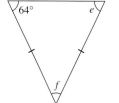

2 Calculate the two identical angles in an isosceles triangle when the other angle is

    a 40°   **b** 70°   **c** 65°

3 An isosceles triangle has an angle of 40°. Sketch the two different possible triangles that match this description, showing what each angle is.

4 The three angles of an isosceles triangle are x, $x - 6°$ and $x - 6°$. What is the actual size of each angle?

5 The three angles of an isosceles triangle are $8x$, $x + 15°$ and $x + 15°$. What is the actual size of each angle?

6 Given that ABCDEFGHI is a regular nonagon, calculate

    a angle BCD   **b** angle BCA   **c** angle ACD

7 Given that ABCDEFGHIJ is a regular decagon, calculate

    a angle ABC   **b** angle ACD   **c** angle ADE

HOMEWORK 7F

1 For each of these trapeziums, calculate the sizes of the lettered angles.

    a 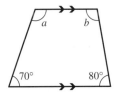   **b** 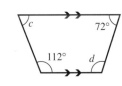   **c**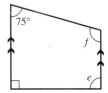

2 For each of these parallelograms, calculate the sizes of the lettered angles.

    a 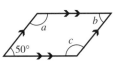   **b** 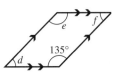   **c**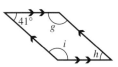

3 For each of these kites, calculate the sizes of the lettered angles.

    a   **b**   **c**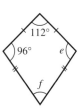

4 For each of these rhombuses, calculate the sizes of the lettered angles.

    a 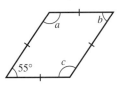   **b**   **c**

5 Calculate the values of x and y in each of these shapes.

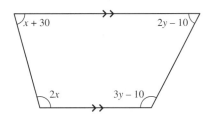

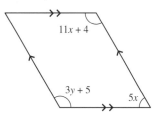

 ★6 Find the value of x in each of these quadrilaterals with the following angles and hence state the type of quadrilateral it is.

  a $x + 10°, x + 30°, x - 30°, x - 50°$ **b** $x°, x - 10°, 3x - 15°, 3x - 15°$

! **7** **a** What do the interior angles of a quadrilateral add up to?

  b Use the fact that the angles of a triangle add up to $180°$, to prove that the sum of the interior angles of any quadrilateral is $360°$.

Chapter 8 Transformation geometry

 ## HOMEWORK 8A

1 State whether each pair of triangles below is congruent, giving the reasons if they are.

  a

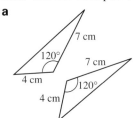

  b

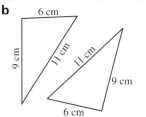

  c

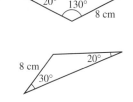

2 Draw a square ABCD. Draw in the diagonals AC and BD. Which triangles are congruent to each other?

3 Draw a kite EFGH. Draw in the diagonals EG and FH. Which triangles are congruent to each other?

4 Draw a rhombus ABCD. Draw in the diagonals AC and BD. Which triangles are congruent to each other?

5 Draw an equilateral triangle ABC. Draw the lines from each vertex to the mid-point of the opposite side. These three lines should all cross at the same point T inside the triangle. Which triangles are congruent to each other?

1 Describe with vectors these translations.

   i A to B   **ii** A to C   **iii** A to D   **iv** B to A   **v** B to C   **vi** B to D

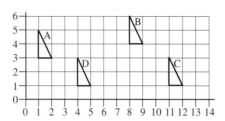

2 **a** On a grid showing values of *x* and *y* from 0 to 10, draw the triangle with co-ordinates A(4, 4), B(5, 7) and C(6, 5).

   b Draw the image of ABC after a translation with vector $\binom{3}{2}$. Label this P.

   c Draw the image of ABC after a translation with vector $\binom{4}{-3}$. Label this Q.

   d Draw the image of ABC after a translation with vector $\binom{-4}{3}$. Label this R.

   e Draw the image of ABC after a translation with vector $\binom{-3}{-2}$. Label this S.

3 Using your diagram from Question **2**, describe the translation that will move

   a P to Q   **b** Q to R   **c** R to S   **d** S to P

   e R to P   **f** S to Q   **g** R to Q   **h** P to S

1 Copy each shape on squared paper and draw its image after a reflection in the given mirror line.

a

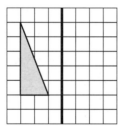

b

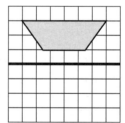

c

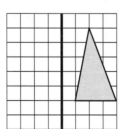

d

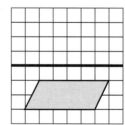

2   Draw each of these figures on squared paper and then draw the reflection of the figure in the mirror line.

a
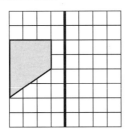

b
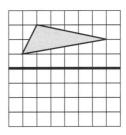

c
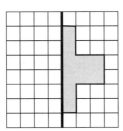

d
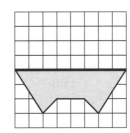

★**3**   Copy this diagram on squared paper.

a   Reflect the triangle ABC in the *x*-axis. Label the image R.

b   Reflect the triangle ABC in the *y*-axis. Label the image S.

c   What special name is given to figures that are exactly the same shape and size?

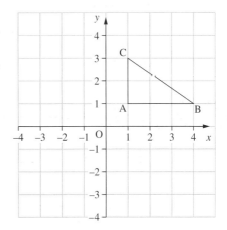

4   **a**   Draw a pair of axes with the *x*-axis from –5 to 5 and the *y*-axis from –5 to 5.

b   Draw the triangle with coordinates A(1, 1), B(5, 5), C(3, 4).

c   Reflect triangle ABC in the *x*-axis. Label the image P.

d   Reflect triangle P in the *y*-axis. Label the image Q.

e   Reflect triangle Q in the *x*-axis. Label the image R.

f   Describe the reflection that will transform triangle ABC onto triangle R.

1 Copy each of these diagrams on squared paper. Draw its image using the given rotation about the centre of rotation A. Using tracing paper may help.

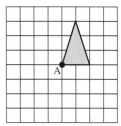

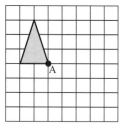

a $\frac{1}{2}$ turn

b $\frac{1}{4}$ turn clockwise

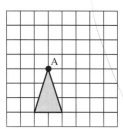

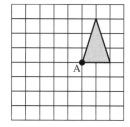

c $\frac{1}{4}$ turn anticlockwise

d $\frac{3}{4}$ turn clockwise

2 Copy each of these flags on squared paper. Draw its image using the given rotation about the centre of rotation A. Using tracing paper may help.

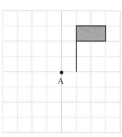

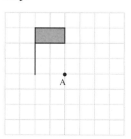

a 180° turn

b 90° turn clockwise

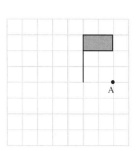

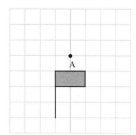

c 90° turn anticlockwise

d 270° turn clockwise

★3 Copy this T-shape on squared paper.

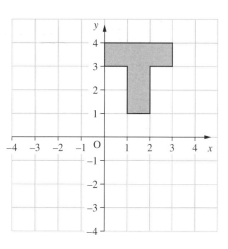

  a Rotate the shape 90° clockwise about the origin O. Label the image P.

  b Rotate the shape 180° clockwise about the origin O. Label the image Q.

  c Rotate the shape 270° clockwise about the origin O. Label the image R.

  d What rotation takes R back to the original shape?

★4 Copy this square ABCD on squared paper.

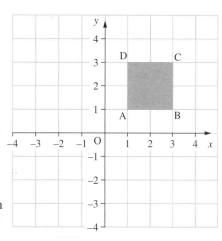

  a Write down the co-ordinates of the vertices of the square ABCD.

  b Rotate the square ABCD through 90° clockwise about the origin O. Label the image S. Write down the co-ordinates of the vertices of the square S.

  c Rotate the square ABCD through 180° clockwise about the origin O. Label the image T. Write down the co-ordinates of the vertices of the square T.

  d Rotate the square ABCD through 270° clockwise about the origin O. Label the image U. Write down the co-ordinates of the vertices of the square U.

  e What do you notice about the co-ordinates of the four squares?

HOMEWORK 8E

1 Copy each figure below with its centre of enlargement, leaving plenty of space for the enlargement. Then enlarge them by the given scale factor, using the ray method.

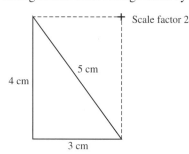

2 Copy each figure below with its centre of enlargement, leaving plenty of space for the enlargement. Then enlarge them by the given scale factor, using the co-ordinate method.

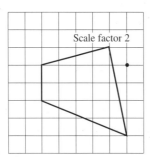

Scale factor 2

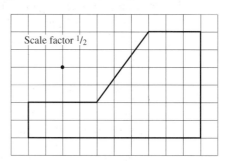

Scale factor $^1/_2$

1 Describe fully the transformation that will move

   a T_1 to T_2 **b** T_1 to T_6 **c** T_2 to T_3 **d** T_6 to T_2

   e T_6 to T_5 **f** T_5 to T_4 **g** T_1 to T_5

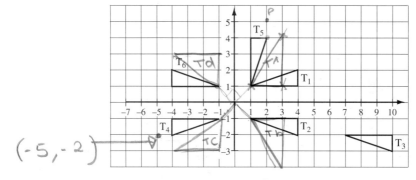

$(-5, -2)$

2 **a** Plot a triangle T with vertices (1, 1), (3, 1), (3, 4).

   b Reflect triangle T in the x-axis and label the image T_b.

   c Rotate triangle T_b 90° clockwise about the origin and label the image T_c.

   d Reflect triangle T_c in the x-axis and label the image T_d.

   e Describe fully the transformation that will move triangle T_d back to triangle T.
     rotation   90° clockwise   about   origin

3 The point P(2, 5) is reflected in the x-axis, then rotated by 90° clockwise about the origin. What are the co-ordinates of the image of P?

Chapter 9   Constructions

1 Draw sketches to illustrate the following situations and then give the back bearing for each one.

   a Hellaby is on a bearing of 030° from Dronfield.

   b Preston is on a bearing of 075° from Liverpool.

   c Yarmouth is on a bearing of 110° from Norwich.

d Totley is on a bearing of 160° from Ecclesall.

e Sheffield is on a bearing of 205° from Wath.

f Bretton is on a bearing of 230° from Wakefield

g Leicester is on a bearing of 280° from Peterborough.

h Eyam is on a bearing of 320° from Chesterfield.

2 A is due west from B. C is due south from B. A is on a bearing of 300° from C. Sketch the layout of the three points A, B and C.

3 A ship is sailing on a cruise from a port on a bearing of 215° when the captain is asked to return to port straight away. The boat must turn round and sail back on what bearing?

4 A pilot was asked to fly in a special formation, that was to fly the three sides of an equilateral triangle.

a Assuming he started by flying due north, give two different ways in which he could complete the equilateral triangle.

b Assuming he started flying on a bearing of 070°, give two different ways in which he could complete the equilateral triangle.

HOMEWORK 9B

1 Accurately draw each of the following triangles.

a

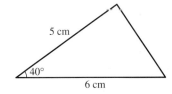

b

c

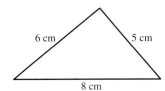

d

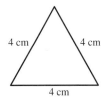

e

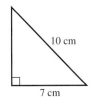

2 Draw a triangle ABC with AB = 6 cm, ∠A = 60° and ∠B = 50°.

3

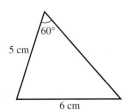

Explain why you can or cannot draw this triangle accurately.

4 a Accurately draw the shape on the right.
b What is the name of the shape you have drawn?

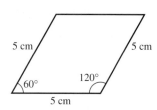

1 Draw a line 8 cm long. Bisect it with a pair of compasses. Check your accuracy by seeing if each half is 4 cm.

2 a Draw any triangle.
b On each side construct the line bisector. All your line bisectors should intersect at the same point.
c See if you can use this point as the centre of a circle that fits perfectly inside the triangle.

3 a Draw a circle with a radius of about 4 cm.
b Draw a quadrilateral such that the vertices (corners) of the quadrilateral are on the circumference of the circle.
c Bisect two of the sides of the quadrilateral. Your bisectors should meet at the centre of the circle.

4 a Draw any angle.
b Construct the angle bisector.
c Check how accurate you have been by measuring each half.

★5 The diagram shows a park with two ice-cream sellers A and B. People always go to the ice-cream seller nearest to them. Shade the region of the park from which people go to ice-cream seller B.

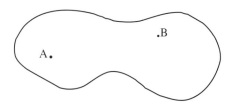

1 Construct these triangles accurately without using a protractor.

2 a Without using a protractor, construct a square of side 5 cm.
b See how accurate you have been by constructing an angle bisector on any of the right-angles and seeing whether this also cuts through the opposite right-angle.

3 With ruler and compasses only, construct an angle of 45°.

4   With ruler and compasses only, construct an angle of 30°.

5   **a**   Draw a line 8 cm long. Call it AB.
    b   At the point A construct an angle of 60°.
    c   At the point B construct an angle of 45°.
    d   Label the point where the two lines meet C.
    e   Measure AC and BC.

★6   **a**   Draw an accurate triangle ABC using only a
        ruler and compasses.
    b   Measure the side BC.

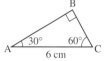

Chapter 10   Shape and symmetry

1   For each shape listed below, find out how many lines of symmetry it has and what the
order of rotational symmetry is.
    a   A rectangle.
    b   A regular pentagon.
    c   A race track.
    d   An isosceles triangle with one angle 90°.
    e   A parallelogram.
    f   An arc of a circle.
    g   A 3,4,5 triangle.

2   Try to draw the following. If you think it's impossible, say so.
    a   A triangle with one line of symmetry.
    b   A triangle with two lines of symmetry.
    c   A triangle with three lines of symmetry.
    d   A triangle with four lines of symmetry.
    e   A triangle with no lines of symmetry.

3   Try to draw the following. If you think it's impossible, say so.
    a   A quadrilateral with one line of symmetry.
    b   A quadrilateral with two lines of symmetry.
    c   A quadrilateral with three lines of symmetry.
    d   A quadrilateral with four lines of symmetry.
    e   A quadrilateral with no lines of symmetry.

4   Can you draw a shape that has an even rotational symmetry, but an odd number of lines
of symmetry. If not, why not?

1 Draw accurately each of these cuboids on an isometric grid.

a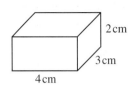

b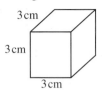

2 Draw accurately each of these 3-D shapes on an isometric grid.

a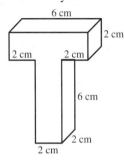

b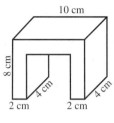

3 For each of the following 3-D shapes, draw on squared paper
    i the plan   **ii** the front elevation   **iii** the side elevation.

a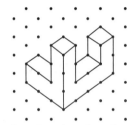

b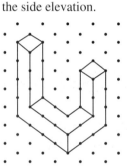

1 **a** Draw a sketch to illustrate a tessellation of a right-angled triangle.
   b Draw another tessellation using the same triangle.
   c How many different tessellations could be made using this triangle?

2 **a** Draw a sketch to illustrate a tessellation of a parallelogram.
   b Draw another tessellation using the same parallelogram.
   c How many different tessellations could be made using this parallelogram?

3 **a** How many different tessellations can be made from a regular pentagon?
   b How many different tessellations can be made from a regular hexagon?
   c How many different tessellations can be made from a regular decagon?

4 Draw a tessellation from a pentagon.

5 Prove that a regular octagon will not tessellate.

6 Show that any quadrilateral will tessellate.

7 **a** Draw a quadrilateral.
   b Change each line on the quadrilateral so that it has rotational symmetry of order 2.
   c Show that this shape will tessellate.

1 Describe the symmetries of
    a a prism with a regular pentagon as its regular cross-section
    b a prism with a regular nonagon as its regular cross-section.

2 How many planes of symmetry do the following have?
    a A single ladder.   **b** A saucer.   **c** A cup.
    d A fork.   **e** An electric toaster.   **f** A seagull.

3 A prism with an isosceles triangle as its regular cross-section has 2 planes of symmetry and one axis of rotational symmetry. Draw diagrams to illustrate this.

4 A prism with an equilateral triangle as its regular cross-section has 4 planes of symmetry and 4 axes of rotational symmetry. Draw diagrams to illustrate this.

5 Using four identical cubes placed together so that whole faces are touching, how many different symmetrical shapes can be made?

6 Sketch a solid that has the following rotational symmetries (ignore plane symmetry).
    a One axis of symmetry of order 3.
    b One axis of symmetry of order 4.
    c Two axes of symmetry, one order 2, the other order 8.

Chapter 11   Properties of number, indices and standard form

1 Write out the first five multiples of:
    a 4   **b** 6   **c** 8   **d** 12   **e** 15
    Remember: the first multiple is the number itself.

2 From the list of numbers below
    28   19   36   43   64   53   77   66   56   60   15   29   61   45   51
    write down those that are:
    a multiples of 4   **b** multiples of 5   **c** multiples of 8   **d** multiples of 11.

3 Use your calculator to see which of the numbers below are
    a multiples of 7   **b** multiples of 9   **c** multiples of 12.
    225   252   361   297   162   363   161   289   224   205   312   378   315   182   369

4 Find the biggest number smaller than 200 that is
    a a multiple of 2   **b** a multiple of 4   **c** a multiple of 5   **d** a multiple of 8
    e a multiple of 9.

5 Find the smallest number that is a multiple of 3 and bigger than
    a 10   **b** 100   **c** 1000   **d** 10 000   **e** 1 000 000 000

1 Draw a factor tree for each of the following numbers.

    a 24   **b** 36   **c** 48   **d** 60   **e** 75   **f** 80

2 Draw four factor trees for 72. Each one must have a different set of numbers on the branches.

3 How many different factor trees could you draw for the number 36?

4 Draw a symmetrical factor tree for the number 144.

5 Draw a symmetrical factor tree for the number 100.

6 Prove that only square numbers will create a symmetrical factor tree.

7 Create the factor tree of 1000 with the smallest number of branches possible.

8 What will be the smallest number of branches in the factor tree for one million?

HOMEWORK 11C

1 Write these expressions using power notation. Do not work them out yet.

    a $5 \times 5 \times 5 \times 5$ **b** $7 \times 7 \times 7 \times 7 \times 7$

    c $19 \times 19 \times 19$ **d** $4 \times 4 \times 4 \times 4 \times 4$

    e $1 \times 1 \times 1 \times 1 \times 1 \times 1 \times 1$ **f** $8 \times 8 \times 8 \times 8 \times 8$

    g 6 **h** $11 \times 11 \times 11 \times 11 \times 11 \times 11$

    i $0.9 \times 0.9 \times 0.9 \times 0.9$ **j** $999 \times 999 \times 999$

2 Write these power terms out in full. Do not work them out yet.

    a 4^5 **b** 8^4 **c** 5^3 **d** 9^6 **e** 1^{11}

    f 7^3 **g** 5.2^3 **h** 7.5^3 **i** 7.7^4 **j** $10\,000^3$

3 Using the power key on your calculator (or another method), work out the values of the power terms in Question **1**.

4 Using the power key on your calculator (or another method), work out the values of the power terms in Question **2**.

 5 Without using a calculator, work out the values of these power terms.

    a 7^0 **b** 9^1 **c** 17^0 **d** 1^{91} **e** 10^5

6 Using your calculator, or otherwise, work out the values of these power terms.

    a $(-2)^3$ **b** $(-1)^{11}$ **c** $(-3)^4$ **d** $(-5)^3$ **e** $(-10)^6$

 7 Without using a calculator, write down the answers to these.

    a $(-4)^2$ **b** $(-5)^3$ **c** $(-3)^4$ **d** $(-2)^5$ **e** $(-1)^6$

HOMEWORK 11D

1 Write these as single powers of 7.

    a $7^3 \times 7^2$ **b** $7^3 \times 7^6$ **c** $7^4 \times 7^3$ **d** 7×7^5 **e** $7^5 \times 7^9$ **f** 7×7^7

2 Write these as single powers of 5.

    a $5^6 \div 5^2$ **b** $5^8 \div 5^2$ **c** $5^4 \div 5^3$ **d** $5^5 \div 5^5$ **e** $5^6 \div 5^4$

3 Simplify these and write them as single powers of a.

   a $a^2 \times a$ **b** $a^3 \times a^2$ **c** $a^4 \times a^3$ **d** $a^6 \div a^2$ **e** $a^3 \div a$ **f** $a^5 \div a^4$

4 Simplify these expressions.

   a $3a^4 \times 5a^2$ **b** $3a^4 \times 7a$ **c** $5a^4 \times 6a^2$ **d** $3a^2 \times 4a^7$

   e $5a^4 \times 5a^2 \times 5a^2$

5 Simplify these expressions.

   a $8a^5 \div 2a^2$ **b** $12a^7 \div 4a^2$ **c** $25a^6 \div 5a$ **d** $48a^8 \div 6a^{-1}$

   e $24a^6 \div 8a^{-2}$ **f** $36a \div 6a^5$

6 Simplify these expressions.

   a $3a^3b^2 \times 4a^3b$ **b** $7a^3b^5 \times 2ab^3$ **c** $4a^3b^5 \times 5a^4b^{-1}$

   d $12a^3b^5 \div 4ab$ **e** $24a^3b^5 \div 6a^2b^{-3}$

 7 Use the general rule for dividing powers of the same number

    $a^x \div a^y = a^{x-y}$

   to prove that any number raised to the power -1 is the reciprocal of that number.

HOMEWORK 11E

1 Evaluate the following.

   a 3.5×100 **b** 2.15×10 **c** 6.74×1000 **d** 4.63×10

   e 30.145×10 **f** 78.56×1000 **g** 6.42×10^2 **h** 0.067×10

   i 0.085×10^3 **j** 0.798×10^5 **k** 0.658×1000 **l** 215.3×10^2

   m 0.889×10^6 **n** 352.147×10^2 **o** 37.2841×10^3 **p** 34.28×10^6

2 Evaluate the following.

   a $4538 \div 100$ **b** $435 \div 10$ **c** $76459 \div 1000$ **d** $643.7 \div 10$

   e $4228.7 \div 100$ **f** $278.4 \div 1000$ **g** $246.5 \div 10^2$ **h** $76.3 \div 10$

   i $76 \div 10^3$ **j** $897 \div 10^5$ **k** $86.5 \div 1000$ **l** $1.5 \div 10^2$

   m $0.8799 \div 10^6$ **n** $23.4 \div 10^2$ **o** $7654 \div 10^3$ **p** $73.2 \div 10^6$

3 Evaluate the following.

   a 400×300 **b** 50×4000 **c** 70×200 **d** 30×700

   e $(30)^2$ **f** $(50)^3$ **g** $(200)^2$ **h** 40×150

   i 70×200 **j** 60×5000 **k** 30×250 **l** 700×200

4 Evaluate the following.

   a $4000 \div 800$ **b** $9000 \div 30$ **c** $7000 \div 200$ **d** $8000 \div 200$

   e $2100 \div 700$ **f** $9000 \div 60$ **g** $700 \div 50$ **h** $3500 \div 70$

   i $3000 \div 500$ **j** $30\,000 \div 2000$ **k** $5600 \div 1400$ **l** $6000 \div 30$

5 Evaluate the following.

   a 7.3×10^2 **b** 3.29×10^5 **c** 7.94×10^3 **d** 6.8×10^7

   e $3.46 \div 10^2$ **f** $5.07 \div 10^4$ **g** $2.3 \div 10^4$ **h** $0.89 \div 10^3$

HOMEWORK 11F

1 Write these standard form numbers out in full.

   a 3.5×10^2 **b** 4.15×10 **c** 5.7×10^{-3} **d** 1.46×10

   e 3.89×10^{-2} **f** 4.6×10^3 **g** 2.7×10^2 **h** 8.6×10

   i 4.6×10^3 **j** 3.97×10^5 **k** 3.65×10^{-3} **l** 7.05×10^2

2 Write these numbers in standard form.

a	780	**b**	0.435	**c**	67 800	**d**	7 400 000 000
e	30 780 000 000	**f**	0.000 427 8	**g**	6450	**h**	0.047
i	0.000 12	**j**	96.43	**k**	74.78	**l**	0.004 157 8

In Questions **3** to **7**, write the appropriate numbers given in each question in standard form.

3 In 1990 there were 24 673 000 vehicles licenced in the UK.

4 In 2001 Keith Gordon was one of 15 282 runners to complete the Boston Marathon.

5 In 1990 the total number of passenger kilometres on the British roads was 613 000 000 000.

6 The Sun is 93 million miles away from Earth. The next nearest star to the Earth is Proxima Centuri which is about 24 million million miles away.

7 A Scientist was working with a new particle reported to weigh only 0.000 000 000 000 65 g.

HOMEWORK 11G

1 Find the result of the following, leaving your answer in standard form.

a $(6 \times 10^7) \times (6 \times 10^7)$ **b** $(6 \times 10^3) \times (7 \times 10^7)$

c $(3 \times 10^6) \times (7 \times 10^7)$ **d** $(7.1 \times 10^7) \times (6 \times 10^7)$

e $(9 \times 10^7) \times (6 \times 10^3)$ **f** $(7 \times 10^3) \times (6 \times 10^6)$

g $(6 \times 10^3) \times (3 \times 10^7)$ **h** $(9 \times 10^{11}) \times (3 \times 10^{19})$

i $(3 \times 10^9) \times (9 \times 10^{-7})$ **j** $(6 \times 10^{13}) \times (7 \times 10^{-9})$

2 Find the results of the following, leaving your answers in standard form.

a $(9 \times 10^7) \div (3 \times 10^3)$ **b** $(1.7 \times 10^7) \div (9 \times 10^3)$

c $(7 \times 10^7) \div (1 \times 10^3)$ **d** $(9 \times 10^{-7}) \div (6 \times 10^6)$

e $(5.1 \times 10^9) \div (3 \times 10^1)$ **f** $(7 \times 10^{12}) \div (9 \times 10^{-3})$

g $(9.6 \times 10^6) \div (7 \times 10^3)$ **h** $(3.6 \times 10^{11}) \div (6 \times 10^6)$

i $(6.6 \times 10^3) \div (1.8 \times 10^{-1})$ **j** $(3.1 \times 10^{-9}) \div (3 \times 10^{-7})$

3 Find the results of the following, leaving your answers in standard form.

a $\dfrac{6 \times 10^9}{3 \times 10^7}$ **b** $\dfrac{15 \times 10^6}{3 \times 10^3}$ **c** $\dfrac{7.2 \times 10^{19}}{9 \times 10^7}$

d $\dfrac{1.4 \times 10^7}{7 \times 10^{-3}}$ **e** $\dfrac{3.5 \times 10^7}{7 \times 10^7}$ **f** $\dfrac{3 \times 10^{-6}}{6 \times 10^{-9}}$

4 $p = 7 \times 10^6$ and $q = 1 \times 10^7$. Find the value of the following, leaving your answer in standard form.

a $p \times q$ **b** $p \div q$ **c** $p + q$ **d** $q - p$ **e** $\dfrac{q}{p}$

Chapter 12   Algebra 2

HOMEWORK 12A

Solve the following pairs of simultaneous equations

1 $5x + y = 17$
       $3x + y = 11$

2 $3x + 2y = 17$
       $5x + 2y = 27$

3 $3x - y = 7$
       $5x + y = 17$

4 $5x - 4y = 27$
       $2x - 4y = 12$

★**5**   Two numbers x and y have a sum of 16 and a difference of 9.
   a   Set up a pair of simultaneous equations connecting x and y.
   b   Solve your equations for x and y.

HOMEWORK 12B

Solve the following pairs of simultaneous equations

1 $3x + 2y = 12$
       $4x - y = 5$

2 $4x + 3y = 37$
       $2x + y = 17$

3 $2x + 3y = 19$
       $6x + 2y = 22$

4 $5x - 2y = 14$
       $3x - y = 9$

★**5**   Four cups of tea and three biscuits cost £3.35.
   Three cups of tea and one biscuit cost £2.20.
   Let x be the cost of a cup of tea and y be the cost of a biscuit.
   a   Set up a pair of simultaneous equations connecting x and y.
   b   Solve your equations for x and y and find the cost of five cups of tea and four biscuits.

HOMEWORK 12C

Solve the following simultaneous equations.

1 $6x + 5y = 23$
       $5x + 3y = 18$

2 $3x - 4y = 13$
       $2x + 3y = 20$

3 $8x - 2y = 14$
       $6x + 4y = 27$

4 $5x + 2y = 33$
       $4x + 5y = 23$

★**5**   It costs two adults and three children £28.50 to go to the cinema.
   It costs three adults and two children £31.50 to go to the cinema.
   Let the price of an adult ticket be £x and the price of a child's ticket be £y.
   a   Set up a pair of simultaneous equations connecting x and y.
   b   Solve your equations for x and y.

HOMEWORK 12D

Solve the following simultaneous equations.

1 $3x + y = 7$
       $x - y = 5$

2 $5x + 3y = 11$
       $3x + y = 7$

3 $3x + 2y = 9$
       $2x - 3y = 19$

4 $2x - 5y = 10$
       $4x - 3y = 13$

You may find a calculator useful for these questions.

5 $3x + 2y = 2$
       $2x + 6y = 27$

6 $4x + 2y = 3$
       $3x + 4y = 5$

7 $3x - 4y = 2.5$
       $2x + 2y = 7.5$

8 $4x + y = 5$
       $3x + 2y = 4$

★9 Paul sold 50 tickets for a concert. He sold x tickets at £3 each and y tickets at £4.50 each. He collected £183.
   i   Write down two equations connecting x and y.
   ii Solve these simultaneous equations to find how many of each kind of ticket he sold.

HOMEWORK 12E

Read each situation carefully, then make a pair of simultaneous equations in order to solve the problem.

1 A book and a CD cost £14.00 together. The CD costs £7 more than the book. How much does each cost?

2 10 second-class and six first-class stamps cost £4.24. 8 second-class and 10 first-class stamps cost £4.90. How much do I pay for 3 second-class and 4 first-class stamps?

3 6 cans of Coke and 5 chocolate bars cost £4.37. 3 cans of Coke and 2 chocolate bars cost £2.00. How much would 2 cans of Coke and a chocolate bar cost?

4 Three bags of sugar and four bags of rice weigh 12 kg. Five bags of sugar and two bags of rice weigh 13 kg. What would two bags of sugar and five bags of rice weigh?

5 Two cakes and three bags of peanuts contain 63 grams of fat. One cake and four bags of peanuts contain 64 grams of fat. How many grams of fat are there in each item?

★6 Wath school buys Basic Scientific calculators and Graphical calculators to sell to students.
An order for 30 Basic Scientific calculators and 25 Graphical calculators came to a total of £1240. Another order for 25 Basic Scientific calculators and 10 Graphical calculators came to a total of £551.25.
Using £x to represent the cost of Basic Scientific calculators and £y to represent the cost of Graphical calculators, set up and solve a pair of simultaneous equations to find the cost of the next order which will be for 35 Basic Scientific calculators and 15 Graphical calculators.

HOMEWORK 12F

1 Solve the following linear inequalities.

a $x + 3 < 8$	**b** $t - 2 > 6$	**c** $p + 3 \geq 11$
d $4x - 5 < 7$	**e** $3y + 4 \leq 22$	**f** $2t - 5 > 13$
g $\dfrac{x + 3}{2} < 8$	**h** $\dfrac{y + 4}{3} \leq 5$	**i** $\dfrac{t - 2}{5} \geq 7$
j $2(x - 3) < 14$	**k** $4(3x + 2) \leq 32$	**l** $5(4t - 1) \geq 30$
m $3x + 1 \geq 2x - 5$	**n** $6t - 5 \leq 4t + 3$	**o** $2y - 11 \leq y - 5$
p $3x + 2 \geq x + 3$	**q** $4w - 5 \leq 2w + 2$	**r** $2(5x - 1) \leq 2x + 3$

2 Write down the values of x that satisfy each of the following.
   a $x - 2 \leq 3$, where x is a positive integer.
   b $x + 3 < 5$, where x is a positive, even integer.
   c $2x - 14 < 38$, where x is a square number.
   d $4x - 6 \leq 15$, where x is a positive, odd number.
   e $2x + 3 < 25$, where x is a positive, prime number.

3 Solve the following linear inequalities.

a $9 < 4x + 1 < 13$ **b** $2 < 3x - 1 < 11$ **c** $-3 < 4x + 5 \le 21$

d $2 \le 3x - 4 < 15$ **e** $10 \le 2x + 3 < 18$ **f** $-5 \le 4x - 7 \le 8$

g $3 \le 5x - 7 \le 13$ **h** $8 \le 2x + 3 < 19$ **i** $7 \le 5x + 3 < 24$

HOMEWORK 12G

1 Write down the inequality that is represented by each diagram below.

a   **b**   **c**

d   **e**   **f**

2 Draw diagrams to illustrate the following.

a $x \le 2$ **b** $x > -3$ **c** $x \ge 0$ **d** $x < 4$

e $x \ge -3$ **f** $1 < x \le 4$ **g** $-2 \le x \le 4$ **h** $-2 < x < 3$

3 Solve the following inequalities and illustrate their solutions on number lines.

a $x + 5 \ge 9$ **b** $x + 4 < 2$ **c** $x - 2 \le 3$ **d** $x - 5 > -2$

e $4x + 3 \le 9$ **f** $5x - 4 \ge 16$ **g** $2x - 1 > 13$ **h** $3x + 6 < 3$

i $3(2x + 1) < 15$ **j** $\dfrac{x + 1}{2} \le 2$ **k** $\dfrac{x - 3}{3} > 7$ **l** $\dfrac{x + 6}{4} \ge 1$

4 Solve the following inequalities and illustrate their solutions on number lines.

a $\dfrac{5x + 2}{2} > 3$ **b** $\dfrac{3x - 4}{5} \le 1$ **c** $\dfrac{4x + 3}{2} \ge 11$ **d** $\dfrac{2x - 5}{4} < 2$

e $\dfrac{8x + 2}{3} \le 2$ **f** $\dfrac{7x + 9}{5} > -1$ **g** $\dfrac{x - 2}{3} \ge -3$ **h** $\dfrac{5x - 2}{4} \le -1$

HOMEWORK 12H

Solve the following inequalities, showing their solutions on number lines.

1 $x^2 \le 9$ **2** $x^2 > 36$ **3** $x^2 < 100$ **4** $x^2 \ge 4$

5 $x^2 \ge 25$ **6** $x^2 - 1 > 15$ **7** $x^2 + 2 \le 11$ **8** $x^2 + 3 > 3$

9 $x^2 + 6 > 7$ **10** $x^2 - 4 \ge 21$ **11** $2x^2 - 3 > 5$ **12** $x^2 - 3 < 6$

13 $5x^2 + 3 \le 17$ **14** $2x^2 - 5 < 27$ **15** $3x^2 - 19 \ge 56$ **16** $x^2 \ge 144$

17 $x^2 < 0.16$ **18** $x^2 \ge 1.21$ **19** $x^2 - 5 \le 88$ **20** $x^2 > 0.25$

HOMEWORK 13A

1 a For each set of data find the mode, the median and the mean.
   i 6, 4, 5, 6, 2, 3, 2, 4, 5, 6, 1
   ii 14, 15, 15, 16, 15, 15, 14, 16, 15, 16, 15
   iii 31, 34, 33, 32, 46, 29, 30, 32, 31, 32, 33
b For each set of data decide which average is the best one to use and give a reason.

2 A supermarket sells oranges in bags of ten.
   The weights of each orange in a selected bag were as follows:
   134 g, 135 g, 142 g, 153 g, 156 g, 132 g, 135 g, 140 g, 148 g, 155 g
   a Find the mode, the median and the mean for the weight of the oranges.
   b The supermarket wanted to state the average weight on each bag they sold. Which of the three averages would you advise the supermarket to use? Explain why.

★3 The weights, in kilograms, of players in a school football team are as follows:
   68, 72, 74, 68, 71, 78, 53, 67, 72, 77, 70
   a Find the median weight of the team.
   b Find the mean weight of the team.
   c Which average is the better one to use? Explain why.

★4 Jez is a member of a pub quiz team and, in the last eight games, his total points were:
   62, 58, 24, 47, 64, 52, 60, 65
   a Find the median for the number of points he scored over the eight weeks.
   b Find the mean for the number of points he scored over the eight weeks.
   c The team captain wanted to know the average for each member of the team. Which average would Jez use? Give a reason for your answer.

HOMEWORK 13B

1 Find **i** the mode, **ii** the median and **iii** the mean from each frequency table below.
   a A survey of the collar sizes of all the male staff in a school gave these results.

Collar size	12	13	14	15	16	17	18
Number of staff	1	3	12	21	22	8	1

   b A survey of the number of TVs in pupils homes gave these results.

Number of TVs	1	2	3	4	5	6	7
Frequency	12	17	30	71	96	74	25

2 A survey of the number of pets in each family of a school gave these results.

Number of pets	0	1	2	3	4	5
Frequency	28	114	108	16	15	8

   a Each child at the school is shown in the data, how many children are at the school?
   b Calculate the median number of pets in a family.
   c How many families have less than the median number of pets?
   d Calculate the mean number of pets in a family. Give your answer to 1 dp.

1   Find for each table of values given below
    i   the modal group   ii   an estimate for the mean.

a

Score	0 – 20	21 – 40	41 – 60	61 – 80	81 – 100
Frequency	9	13	21	34	17

b

Cost (£)	0.00 – 10.00	10.01 – 20.00	20.01 – 30.00	30.01 – 40.00	40.01 – 60.00
Frequency	9	17	27	21	14

2   A survey was made to see how long casualty patients had to wait before seeing a doctor.
    The following table summarises the results for one shift.

Time (minutes)	0 – 10	11 – 20	21 – 30	31 – 40	41 – 50	51 – 60	61 – 70
Frequency	1	12	24	15	13	9	5

a   How many patients were seen by a doctor in the survey of this shift?
b   Estimate the mean waiting time taken per patient.
c   Which average would the hospital use for the average waiting time?
d   What percentage of patients did the doctors see within the hour?

1   a   The table shows the ages of 300 people at the cinema.

Age, x years	$0 \leq x < 10$	$10 \leq x < 15$	$15 \leq x < 20$	$20 \leq x < 30$	$30 \leq x < 60$
Frequency	25	85	115	45	30

Draw a histogram to show the data.
b   At another film show this was the distribution of ages.

Age, x years	$15 \leq x < 20$	$20 \leq x < 30$	$30 \leq x < 40$	$40 \leq x < 60$	$60 \leq x < 80$
Frequency	35	120	130	50	15

Draw a histogram to show this data.
c   Comment on the differences between the distributions.

2   The table shows the times taken by 50 children to complete a multiplication square.

Time, s seconds	$10 \leq s < 20$	$20 \leq s < 25$	$25 \leq s < 30$	$30 \leq s < 40$	$40 \leq s < 60$
Frequency	3	9	28	6	4

a   Draw a frequency polygon for this data.
b   Calculate an estimate of the mean of the data.
c   Draw a vertical line on the histogram at the mean value.
d   What is the significance of this line in relation to the size of the bars of the histogram?

★3 The waiting times for customers at a supermarket checkout are shown in the table.
  a Draw a histogram of these waiting times.
  b Estimate the mean waiting time.

Waiting time (minutes)	Frequency
$0 \leq x < 1$	15
$1 \leq x < 3$	7
$3 \leq x < 4$	12
$4 \leq x < 5$	15
$5 \leq x < 10$	12

HOMEWORK 13E

1 Draw pie charts to represent the following sets of data.

a

Day	Monday	Tuesday	Wednesday	Thursday	Friday
Number	100	65	80	95	20

b

Season	Winter	Spring	Summer	Autumn
Number	30	35	75	40

c

Year	1997	1998	1999	2000	2001
Attendance	1500	3300	5700	6300	7200

2 The number of passengers travelling on a particular line over a period of five years were recorded as:

Year	1997	1998	1999	2000	2001
Passengers	68 000	78 000	88 000	17 000	19 000

  a Illustrate this information on a pie chart.
  b Illustrate this information on a frequency polygon.
  c Illustrate this information on a bar chart.
  d Which diagram best illustrates the data?

3 In one class there are 27 students that are right-handed, and only three that are left-handed. Illustrate this data in the best way possible.

HOMEWORK 13F

1 'People like the video hire centre to be open 24 hours a day.'
  a To see whether this statement is true, design a data collection sheet which will allow you to capture data while standing outside a video hire centre.
  b Does it matter at which time you collect your data?

2 The Youth Club wanted to know which types of activities it should plan, e.g. craft, swimming, squash, walking, disco etc.
  a Design a data collection sheet which you could use to ask the pupils in your school which activities they would want in a Youth Club.
  b Invent the first 30 entries on the chart.

★3 What types of film do your age group watch at the cinema the most? Is it comedy, romance, sci-fi, action, suspense or something else?
  a Design a data collection sheet to be used in a survey of your age group.
  b Invent the first thirty entries on your sheet.

HOMEWORK 13G

1 Design a questionnaire to test the following statement.
  'Young people aged 16 and under will not tell their parents when they have been drinking alcohol, but the over 16s will always let their parents know.'

★2 'Boys will use the Internet almost everyday but girls will only use it about once a week.'
  Design a questionnaire to test this statement.

★3 Design a questionnaire to test the following hypothesis.
  'When you are in your twenties, you watch less TV than any other age group.'

4 While on holiday in Wales, I noticed that in the supermarkets there were a lot more women than men, and even then, the only men I did see were over 65.
  a Write down a hypothesis from the above observation.
  b Design a questionnaire to test your hypothesis.

Chapter 14   Algebra 3

HOMEWORK 14A

Evaluate these expressions, writing them as simply as possible.

1 $3 \times 4t$	**2** $2 \times 5y$	**3** $4y \times 2$	**4** $3w \times 3$
5 $4t \times t$	**6** $6b \times b$	**7** $3w \times w$	**8** $6y \times 2y$
9 $5p \times p$	**10** $4t \times 32t$	**11** $5m \times 4m$	**12** $6t \times 4t$
13 $m \times 7t$	**14** $5y \times w$	**15** $8t \times q$	**16** $n \times 69t$
17 $5 \times 6q$	**18** $5f \times 2$	**19** $6 \times 3k$	**20** $5 \times 7r$
21 $t^2 \times t$	**22** $p \times p^2$	**23** $5m \times m^2$	**24** $3t^2 \times t$
25 $4n \times 2n^2$	**26** $5r^2 \times 4r$	**27** $t^2 \times t^2$	**28** $k^3 \times k^2$
29 $8n^2 \times 2n^3$	**30** $4t^3 \times 3t^4$	**31** $7a^4 \times 2a^3$	**32** $k^5 \times 3k^2$
33 $-k^2 \times -k$	**34** $-5y \times -2y$	**35** $-3d^2 \times -6d$	**36** $-2p^4 \times 6p^2$
37 $5mq \times q$	**38** $4my \times 3m$	**39** $4mt \times 3m$	**40** $5qp \times 2qp$

HOMEWORK 14B

Expand these expressions.

1 $3(4 + m)$	**2** $6(3 + p)$	**3** $4(4 - y)$	**4** $3(6 + 7k)$
5 $4(3 - 5f)$	**6** $2(4 - 23w)$	**7** $7(g + h)$	**8** $4(2k + 4m)$
9 $6(2d - n)$	**10** $t(t + 5)$	**11** $m(m + 4)$	**12** $k(k - 2)$
13 $g(4g + 1)$	**14** $y(3y - 21)$	**15** $p(7 - 8p)$	**16** $2m(m + 5)$
17 $3t(t - 2)$	**18** $3k(5 - k)$	**19** $2g(4g + 3)$	**20** $4h(2h - 3)$
21 $2t(6 - 5t)$	**22** $4d(3d + 5e)$	**23** $3y(4y + 5k)$	**24** $6m^2(3m - p)$
25 $y(y^2 + 7)$	**26** $h(h^3 + 9)$	**27** $k(k^2 - 4)$	**28** $3t(t^2 + 3)$
29 $5h(h^3 - 2)$	**30** $4g(g^3 - 3)$	**31** $5m(2m^2 + m)$	**32** $2d(4d^2 - d^3)$
33 $4w(3w^2 + t)$	**34** $3a(5a^2 - b)$	**35** $2p(7p^3 - 8m)$	**36** $m^2(3 + 5m)$
37 $t^3(t + 3t)$	**38** $g^2(4t - 3g^2)$	**39** $2t^2(7t + m)$	**40** $3h^2(4h + 5g)$

1 Simplify these expressions.

   a $5t + 4t$ **b** $4m + 3m$ **c** $6y + y$ **d** $2d + 3d + 5d$

   e $7e - 5e$ **f** $6g - 3g$ **g** $3p - p$ **h** $5t - t$

   i $t^2 + 4t^2$ **j** $5y^2 - 2y^2$ **k** $4ab + 3ab$ **l** $5a^2d - 4a^2d$

2 Expand and simplify.

   a $3(2 + t) + 4(3 + t)$ **b** $6(2 + 3k) + 2(5 + 3k)$ **c** $5(2 + 4m) + 3(1 + 4m)$

   d $3(4 + y) + 5(1 + 2y)$ **e** $5(2 + 3f) + 3(6 - f)$ **f** $7(2 + 5g) + 2(3 - g)$

3 Expand and simplify.

   a $4(3 + 2h) - 2(5 + 3h)$ **b** $5(3g + 4) - 3(2g + 5)$ **c** $3(4y + 5) - 2(3y + 2)$

   d $3(5t + 2) - 2(4t + 5)$ **e** $5(5k + 2) - 2(4k - 3)$ **f** $4(4e + 3) - 2(5e - 4)$

4 Expand and simplify.

   a $m(5 + p) + p(2 + m)$ **b** $k(4 + h) + h(5 + 2k)$ **c** $t(1 + 2n) + n(3 + 5t)$

   d $p(5q + 1) + q(3p + 5)$ **e** $2h(3 + 4j) + 3j(h + 4)$ **f** $3y(4t + 5) + 2t(1 + 4y)$

5 Expand and simplify.

   a $t(2t + 5) + 2t(4 + t)$ **b** $3y(4 + 3y) + y(6y - 5)$ **c** $5w(3w + 2) + 4w(3 - w)$

   d $4p(2p + 3) - 3p(2 - 3p)$ **e** $4m(m - 1) + 3m(4 - m)$ **f** $5d(3 - d) + d(2d - 1)$

6 Expand and simplify.

   a $5a(3b + 2a) + a(2a^2 + 3c)$ **b** $4y(3w + y^2) + y(3y - 4t)$

Factorise the following expressions.

  1 $9m + 12t$ **2** $9t + 6p$ **3** $4m + 12k$ **4** $4r + 6t$

  5 $2mn + 3m$ **6** $4g^2 + 3g$ **7** $4w - 8t$ **8** $10p - 6k$

  9 $12h - 10k$ **10** $4mp + 2mk$ **11** $4bc + 6bk$ **12** $8ab + 4ac$

 13 $3y^2 + 4y$ **14** $5t^2 - 3t$ **15** $3d^2 - 2d$ **16** $6m^2 - 3mp$

 17 $3p^2 + 9pt$ **18** $8pt + 12mp$ **19** $8ab - 6bc$ **20** $4a^2 - 8ab$

 21 $8mt - 6pt$ **22** $20at^2 + 12at$ **23** $4b^2c - 10bc$ **24** $4abc + 6bed$

 25 $6a^2 + 4a + 10$ **26** $12ab + 6bc + 9bd$ **27** $6t^2 + 3t + at$

 28 $96mt^2 - 3mt + 69m^2t$ **29** $6ab^2 + 2ab - 4a^2b$ **30** $5pt^2 + 15pt + 5p^2t$

Factorise the following expressions where possible. List those which cannot factorise.

 31 $5m - 6t$ **32** $3m + 2mp$ **33** $t^2 - 5t$ **34** $6pt + 5ab$

 35 $8m^2 - 6mp$ **36** $a^2 + c$ **37** $3a^2 - 7ab$ **38** $4ab + 5cd$

 39 $7ab - 4b^2c$ **40** $3p^2 - 4t^2$ **41** $6m^2t + 9t^2m$ **42** $5mt + 3pn$

Expand the following expressions.

  1 $(x + 2)(x + 5)$ **2** $(t + 3)(t + 2)$ **3** $(w + 4)(w + 1)$

  4 $(m + 6)(m + 2)$ **5** $(k + 2)(k + 4)$ **6** $(a + 3)(a + 1)$

  7 $(x + 3)(x - 1)$ **8** $(t + 6)(t - 4)$ **9** $(w + 2)(w - 3)$

 10 $(f + 1)(f - 4)$ **11** $(g + 2)(g - 5)$ **12** $(y + 5)(y - 2)$

 13 $(x - 4)(x + 3)$ **14** $(p - 3)(p + 2)$ **15** $(k - 5)(k + 1)$

16 $(y - 3)(y + 6)$ **17** $(a - 2)(a + 4)$ **18** $(t - 4)(t + 5)$

19 $(x - 3)(x - 2)$ **20** $(r - 4)(r - 1)$ **21** $(m - 1)(m - 7)$

22 $(g - 5)(g - 3)$ **23** $(h - 6)(h - 2)$ **24** $(n - 2)(n - 8)$

25 $(4 + x)(3 + x)$ **26** $(5 + t)(4 - t)$ **27** $(2 - b)(6 + b)$

28 $(7 - y)(5 - y)$ **29** $(3 + p)(p - 2)$ **30** $(3 - k)(k - 5)$

HOMEWORK 14F

Expand the following expressions.

1 $(3x + 4)(4x + 2)$ **2** $(2y + 1)(3y + 2)$ **3** $(4t + 2)(3t + 6)$

4 $(3t + 2)(2t - 1)$ **5** $(6m + 1)(3m - 2)$ **6** $(5k + 3)(4k - 3)$

7 $(4p - 5)(3p + 4)$ **8** $(6w + 1)(3w + 4)$ **9** $(3a - 4)(5a + 1)$

10 $(5r - 2)(3r - 1)$ **11** $(4g - 1)(3g - 2)$ **12** $(3d - 2)(4d + 1)$

13 $(3 + 4p)(5 + 4p)$ **14** $(3 + 2t)(5 + 3t)$ **15** $(2 + 5p)(3p + 1)$

16 $(7 + 4t)(3 - 2t)$ **17** $(5 + 2n)(4 - n)$ **18** $(3 + 4f)(5f - 1)$

19 $(2 - 3q)(5 + 4q)$ **20** $(3 - p)(2 + 3p)$ **21** $(5 - 3t)(4t + 1)$

22 $(5 - 4r)(3 - 4r)$ **23** $(4 - x)(1 - 5x)$ **24** $(2 - 7m)(2m - 3)$

25 $(x + y)(3x + 5y)$ **26** $(4y + t)(3y - 4t)$ **27** $(5x - 3y)(5x + y)$

28 $(x - 2y)(x - 3y)$ **29** $(4m - 3p)(m + 5p)$ **30** $(t - 4k)(3t - k)$

Try to spot the pattern in each of the following expressions so that you can immediately write down the expansion.

31 $(x + 1)(x - 1)$ **32** $(t + 2)(t - 2)$ **33** $(y + 3)(y - 3)$

34 $(2m + 3)(2m - 3)$ **35** $(4k - 3)(4k + 3)$ **36** $(5h - 1)(5h + 1)$

37 $(3 + 2x)(3 - 2x)$ **38** $(7 + 2t)(7 - 2t)$ **39** $(4 - 5y)(4 + 5y)$

40 $(a + b)(a - b)$ **41** $(3t + k)(3t - k)$ **42** $(m - 3p)(m + 3p)$

43 $(8k + g)(8k - g)$ **44** $(ac + bd)(ac - bd)$ **45** $(x^2 + y^2)(x^2 - y^2)$

HOMEWORK 14G

Expand the following squares.

1 $(x + 4)^2$ **2** $(m + 3)^2$ **3** $(5 + t)^2$ **4** $(2 + p)^2$

5 $(m - 2)^2$ **6** $(t - 4)^2$ **7** $(3 - m)^2$ **8** $(6 - k)^2$

9 $(2x + 1)^2$ **10** $(3t + 2)^2$ **11** $(1 + 4y)^2$ **12** $(2 + m)^2$

13 $(3t - 2)^2$ **14** $(2x - 1)^2$ **15** $(1 - 4t)^2$ **16** $(5 - 4r)^2$

17 $(a + b)^2$ **18** $(x - y)^2$ **19** $(3t + y)^2$ **20** $(m - 2n)^2$

21 $(x + 3)^2 - 4$ **22** $(x - 4)^2 - 25$ **23** $(x + 5)^2 - 36$ **24** $(x - 1)^2 - 1$

HOMEWORK 14H

Factorise the following.

1 $x^2 + 7x + 6$ **2** $t^2 + 4t + 4$ **3** $m^2 + 11m + 10$ **4** $k^2 + 11k + 24$

5 $p^2 + 10p + 24$ **6** $r^2 + 11r + 18$ **7** $w^2 + 9w + 18$ **8** $x^2 + 8x + 12$

9 $a^2 + 13a + 12$ **10** $k^2 - 10k + 21$ **11** $f^2 - 22f + 21$ **12** $b^2 + 35b + 96$

13 $t^2 + 5t + 6$ **14** $m^2 - 5m + 4$ **15** $p^2 - 7p + 10$ **16** $x^2 - 13x + 36$

17 $c^2 - 12c + 32$ **18** $t^2 - 15t + 36$ **19** $y^2 - 14y + 48$ **20** $j^2 - 19j + 48$

21 $p^2 + 8p + 15$ **22** $y^2 + y - 6$ **23** $t^2 + 7t - 8$ **24** $x^2 + 9x - 10$

25 $m^2 - m - 12$ **26** $r^2 + 6r - 7$ **27** $n^2 - 7n - 18$ **28** $m^2 - 20m - 44$

29 $w^2 - 5w - 24$	30 $t^2 + t - 90$	31 $x^2 - x - 72$	32 $t^2 - 18t - 63$
33 $d^2 - 2d + 1$	34 $y^2 + 29y + 100$	35 $t^2 - 10t + 16$	36 $m^2 - 30m + 81$
37 $x^2 - 30x + 144$	38 $d^2 - 4d - 12$	39 $t^2 + t - 20$	40 $q^2 + q - 56$
41 $p^2 - p - 2$	42 $v^2 - 2v - 35$	43 $t^2 - 4t + 3$	44 $m^2 + 3m - 4$
45 $x^2 - 4$	46 $t^2 - 16$	47 $m^2 - 1$	48 $4 - x^2$
49 $25 - t^2$	50 $k^2 - 49$	51 $9 - y^2$	52 $x^2 - 25$
53 $t^2 - 64$	54 $x^2 - y^2$	55 $x^2 - 9y^2$	56 $x^2 - 25y^2$

HOMEWORK 14 I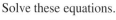

Solve these equations.

1 $(x + 3)(x + 2) = 0$ **2** $(t + 4)(t + 1) = 0$ **3** $(a + 5)(a + 3) = 0$

4 $(x + 4)(x - 1) = 0$ **5** $(x + 2)(x - 5) = 0$ **6** $(t + 3)(t - 4) = 0$

7 $(x - 2)(x + 1) = 0$ **8** $(x - 1)(x + 4) = 0$ **9** $(a - 6)(a + 5) = 0$

10 $(x - 2)(x - 5) = 0$ **11** $(x - 2)(x - 1) = 0$ **12** $(a - 2)(a - 6) = 0$

First factorise, then solve these equations.

13 $x^2 + 6x + 5 = 0$ **14** $x^2 + 9x + 18 = 0$ **15** $x^2 - 7x + 8 = 0$

16 $x^2 - 4x + 21 = 0$ **17** $x^2 + 3x - 10 = 0$ **18** $x^2 + 2x - 15 = 0$

19 $t^2 - 4t - 12 = 0$ **20** $t^2 - 3t - 18 = 0$ **21** $x^2 + x - 2 = 0$

22 $x^2 - 4x + 4 = 0$ **23** $m^2 - 10m + 25 = 0$ **24** $t^2 - 10t + 16 = 0$

25 $t^2 + 7t + 12 = 0$ **26** $k^2 - 3k - 18 = 0$ **27** $a^2 - 20a + 64 = 0$

HOMEWORK 14J

1 $y = mx + c$ **i** Make c the subject.   **ii** Express x in terms of y, m and c.

2 $v = u - 10t$ **i** Make u the subject.   **ii** Express t in terms of v and u.

3 $T = 2x + 3y$ **i** Express x in terms of T and y.   **ii** Make y the subject.

4 $p = q^2$ Make q the subject.

5 $p = q^2 - 3$ Make q the subject.

6 $a = b^2 + c$ Make b the subject.

★**7**   A rocket is fired vertically upwards with an initial velocity of u metres per second. After t seconds the rocket's velocity, v metres per second, is given by the formula $v = u + gt$, where g is a constant.

   a   Calculate v when $u = 120$, $g = -9.8$ and $t = 6$.

   b   Rearrange the formula to express t in terms of v, u, and g.

   c   Calculate t when $u = 100$, $g = -9.8$ and $v = 17.8$.

1 A hire firm hired out large scanners. They used the following graph to approximate what the charges would be.

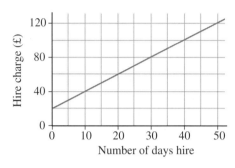

a Use the graph to find the approximate charge for hiring a scanner for
   i 20 days   **ii** 30 days   **iii** 50 days.

b Use the graph to find out how many days hire you would get for a cost of
   i £120   **ii** £100   **iii** £70.

2 A conference centre used the following chart for the approximate cost of a conference based on the number of people attending it.

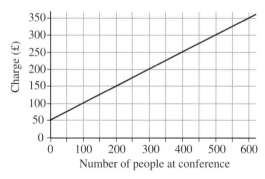

a Use the graph to find the approximate charge for
   i 500 people   **ii** 300 people   **iii** 250 people.

b Use the graph to estimate how many people can attend a conference at the centre for a cost of
   i £250   **ii** £150   **iii** £125.

3 Jayne lost her fuel bill, but while talking to her friends, she found out that:
   Kris who had used 750 units was charged £69.
   Nic who had used 250 units was charged £33.
   Shami who had used 500 units was charged £51.

a Plot the given information and draw a straight-line graph. Use a scale from 0 to 800 on the horizontal units axis, and from £0 to £70 on the vertical cost axis.

b Use your graph to find what Jayne will be charged for 420 units.

1 Joe was travelling in his car to meet his girlfriend. He set off from home at 9.00 pm, and stopped on the way for a break. This distance–time graph illustrates his journey.

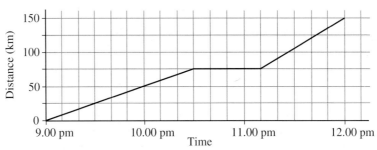

a At what time did he
  i stop for his break   **ii** set off after his break   **iii** get to his meeting place?
b At what average speed was he travelling
  i over the first hour   **ii** over the last hour   **iii** for the whole of his journey?

2 A taxi set off from Hellaby to pick up Jean. It then went on to pick up Jeans's parents. It then travelled further, dropping them all off at a shopping centre. The taxi went on a further 10 km to pick up another party and took them back to Hellaby. This distance–time graph illustrates the journey.

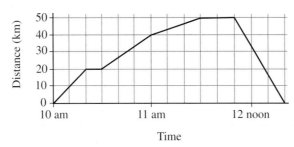

a How far from Hellaby did Jean's parents live?
b How far from Hellaby is the shopping centre?
c What was the average speed of the taxi while only Jean was in the taxi?
d What was the average speed of the taxi back to Hellaby?

3 Grandad took his grandchildren out for a trip. He set off at 1.00 pm and travelled, for half an hour, away from Norwich at an average speed of 60 km/h. They stopped to look at the sea and have an ice cream. At two o'clock, they set off again, travelling for a quarter of an hour at an average speed of 80 km/h. Then they stopped to play on the sand for half an hour. Grandad then drove the grandchildren back home at an average speed of 50 km/h. Draw a travel graph to illustrate this story. Use a horizontal axis to represent time from 1 pm to 4 pm, and a vertical scale from 0 km to 50 km.

1 Calculate the gradient of each line.

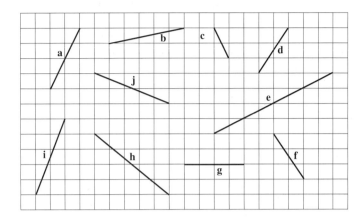

2 Calculate the average speed of the journey represented by each line in the following diagrams. The gradient of each line is the speed.

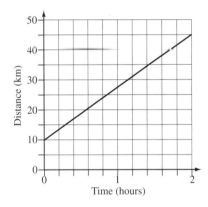

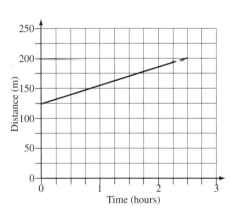

3 This is a conversion graph between ounces and grams.
    a Calculate the gradient of the line.
    b Use the graph to find the number of grams equivalent to 1 ounce.

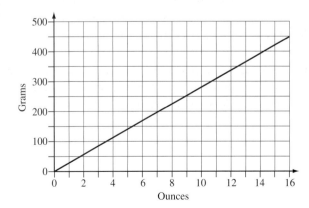

1 This graph illustrates the charges made by an electricity company.

  a Calculate the standing charge (this is the amount paid before any electricity is used).

  b What is the gradient of the line?

  c From your answers to **a** and **b** write down the rule to calculate the total charge for electricity.

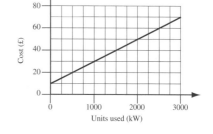

2 This graph illustrates the charges made by a gas company.

  a Calculate the standing charge.

  b What is the gradient of the line?

  c From your answers to **a** and **b** write down the rule to calculate the total charge for gas.

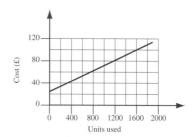

★**3** This graph illustrates the charges made by a phone company.

  a Calculate the standing charge.

  b What is the gradient of the line?

  c From your answers to **a** and **b** write down the rule to calculate the total charge for using this phone company.

Chapter 16   Similarity

1 These diagrams are drawn to scale. What is the scale factor of the enlargement in each case?

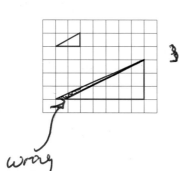

wrong size

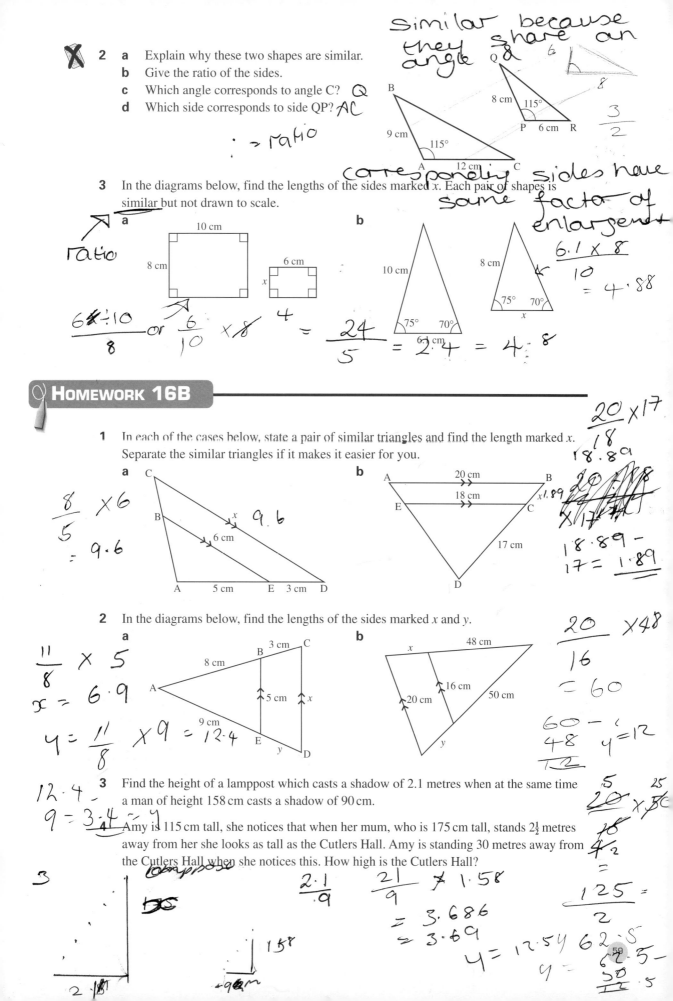

2
  a Explain why these two shapes are similar.
  b Give the ratio of the sides.
  c Which angle corresponds to angle C? Q
  d Which side corresponds to side QP? AC

Handwritten: similar because they share an angle Q

Handwritten: ∴ → ratio

Handwritten: 3/2

Handwritten: corresponding sides have same factor of enlargement

Triangle ABC: 9 cm (AB), 115° at A, 12 cm (AC)
Triangle PQR: 8 cm (PQ), 115° at P, 6 cm (PR)

3 In the diagrams below, find the lengths of the sides marked *x*. Each pair of shapes is similar but not drawn to scale.

Handwritten: ratio

a
Rectangle: 10 cm (top), 8 cm (side)
Smaller rectangle: 6 cm (top), x (side)

Handwritten: 6×÷10 / 8 or 6/10 × 8 = 24/5 = 2.4

b
Triangle: 10 cm, 75°, 70°
Triangle: 8 cm, 75°, 70°, x

Handwritten: 6.1 × 8 / 10 = 4.88

Handwritten: 4 = 24/5 = 6.4 = 4.8

---

1 In each of the cases below, state a pair of similar triangles and find the length marked *x*. Separate the similar triangles if it makes it easier for you.

a
Triangle with C at top, B on left, x marked, 6 cm, A, 5 cm, E, 3 cm, D

Handwritten: 8/5 × 6 = 9.6

Handwritten: 9.6

b
Triangle: A — 20 cm — B, E — 18 cm — C, 17 cm, D

Handwritten: 20 × 17 / 18 = 18.89
x1.89
X 17
18.89 − 17 = 1.89

2 In the diagrams below, find the lengths of the sides marked *x* and *y*.

a
Triangle: B 3 cm C, 8 cm, A, 5 cm, x, 9 cm, E, y, D

Handwritten: 11/8 × 5
x = 6.9
y = 11/8 × 9 = 12.4

Handwritten: 12.4
9 = 3.4 ≈ y

b
Triangle: x, 48 cm, 16 cm, 20 cm, 50 cm, y

Handwritten: 20/16 × 48 = 60
60 − 48 = 12 y = 12

3 Find the height of a lamppost which casts a shadow of 2.1 metres when at the same time a man of height 158 cm casts a shadow of 90 cm.

4 Amy is 115 cm tall, she notices that when her mum, who is 175 cm tall, stands 2½ metres away from her she looks as tall as the Cutlers Hall. Amy is standing 30 metres away from the Cutlers Hall when she notices this. How high is the Cutlers Hall?

Handwritten: 2.1/.9   21/9 × 1.58 = 3.686 = 3.69

Handwritten: 5   25
20/18 × 50
4/2
= 125/2
y = 12.54   62.5
y = 62.5 / 5
30/.5

Handwritten diagram: 158, 90 cm, 2.1

Find the lengths x and y in the diagrams below.

1
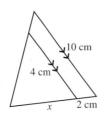

2
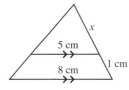

3
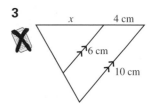

4
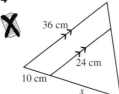

5
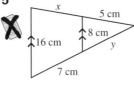

6
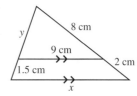

7
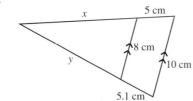

8
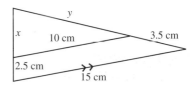

Chapter 17   Pythagoras

HOMEWORK 17A

1   Without doing any drawing, find the value of the **square** of the hypotenuse (marked x).

a
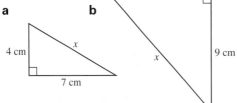

b

c
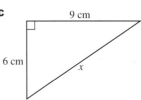

2 Without doing any drawing, find the value of the **square** of the unknown short side (marked x).

a
7 cm
10 cm
x

b
x
12 cm
10 cm

c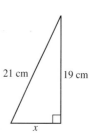
21 cm
19 cm
x

3 Without doing any drawing, find the value of the **square** of the unknown side (marked x).

a
5 cm
7 cm
x

b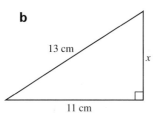
13 cm
x
11 cm

c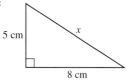
5 cm
x
8 cm

In each of the following triangles, find the hypotenuse, rounding off to a suitable degree of accuracy.

1
4 cm
3 cm

2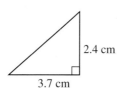
2.4 cm
3.7 cm

3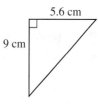
5.6 cm
9 cm

4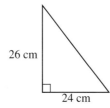
26 cm
24 cm

5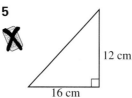
12 cm
16 cm

6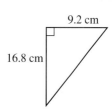
9.2 cm
16.8 cm

★**7** This diagram is not drawn to scale. It shows the cross-section of a swimming pool 50 m long. It is 3.5 m deep at the deep end. The deepest part of the pool is 10 m long.
   a   Calculate the length of the sloping bottom of the pool AB.
   b   The pool is 20 m wide. What is its volume?

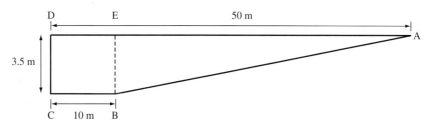
D   E   50 m
3.5 m
C   10 m   B
A

1 In each of the following triangles, find the length of *x* to a suitable degree of accuracy.

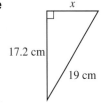

a 27 cm, *x*, 13 cm

b 28 cm, *x*, 17 cm

c 7.2 cm, *x*, 10 cm

d 45 cm, 31 cm, *x*

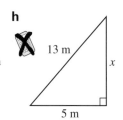

e *x*, 17.2 cm, 19 cm

f 1000 m, *x*, 650 m

g *x*, 2 cm, 1.8 cm

h 13 m, *x*, 5 m

2 In each of the following triangles, find the length of *x* to a suitable degree of accuracy.

a 8 m, *x*, 6 m

b 29 cm, 10 cm, *x*

c 15 m, 33 m, *x*

d 9.5 cm, *x*, 8 cm

★3 The diagram shows the end view of the framework for a sports arena stand. Calculate the length AB.

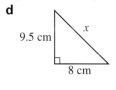

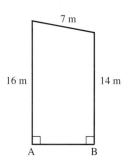

7 m

16 m   14 m

A   B

Without using your calculator, find the value of x in each of the following triangles.

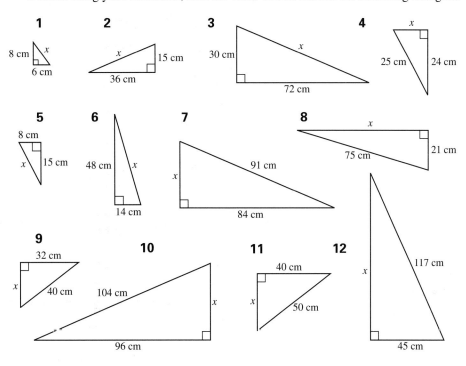

1
8 cm
x
6 cm

2
x
15 cm
36 cm

3
30 cm
x
72 cm

4
x
25 cm
24 cm

5
8 cm
x
15 cm

6
48 cm
x
14 cm

7
91 cm
x
84 cm

8
x
75 cm
21 cm

9
32 cm
x
40 cm

10
104 cm
x
96 cm

11
40 cm
x
50 cm

12
117 cm
x
45 cm

1 A ladder, 15 metres long, leans against a wall. The ladder reaches 12 metres up the wall. How far away from the foot of the wall is the foot of the ladder.

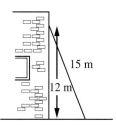

15 m
12 m

2 A rectangle is 3 metres long and 1.2 m wide. How long is the diagonal?

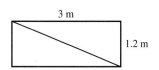

3 m
1.2 m

3 How long is the diagonal of a square with a side of 10 metres?

4 A ship going from a port to a lighthouse steams 8 km east and 6 km north. How far is the lighthouse from the port?

5 At the moment, three towns, A, B and C, are joined by two roads, as in the diagram. The council wants to make a road which runs directly from A to C. How much distance will the new road save?

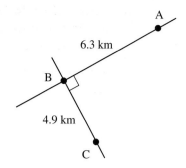

6 An 8-metre ladder is put up against a wall.
   a How far up the wall will it reach when the foot of the ladder is 1 m away from the wall?
   b When it reaches 7 m up the wall, how far is the foot of the ladder away from the wall?

7 How long is the line that joins the two co-ordinates A(1, 3) and B(2, 2)?

8 A rectangle is 4 cm long. The length of its diagonal is 5 cm. What is the area of the rectangle?

9 Is the triangle with sides 9 cm, 40 cm and 41 cm a right-angled triangle?

10 How long is the line that joins the two co-ordinates A(−3, −7), and B(4, 6)?

★11 The diagram shows a voyage from A to position B. The boat sails due east from A for 27 km to position C. The boat then changes course and sails for 30 km to position B. On a map, the distance between A and C is 10.8 cm.
   a Work out the scale of the map.
   b Calculate the distance, in km, of B from A.

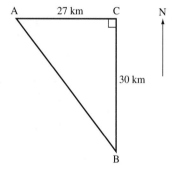

HOMEWORK 17F

1 Calculate the area of these isosceles triangles.

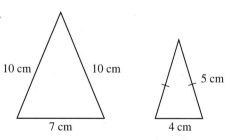

2 Calculate the area of an isosceles triangle whose sides are 10 cm, 10 cm and 8 cm.

3 Calculate the area of an equilateral triangle of side 10 cm.

4 **a** Calculate the area of an equilateral triangle of side 20 cm.
   b Explain why the answer to **4a** is not twice that of Question **3**.

5 An isosceles triangle has sides of 6 cm and 8 cm.

    a Sketch the two isosceles triangles that fit this data.

    b Which of the two triangles has the greater area?

★6 The diagram shows an isosceles triangle of base 10 mm and side 12 mm. Calculate the area of the triangle.

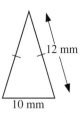

Chapter 18   Trigonometry

HOMEWORK 18A

1 Find these values, rounding off your answers to 3 sf.

    a $\sin 52°$ **b** $\sin 46°$ **c** $\sin 76.3°$ **d** $\sin 90°$

2 Find these values, rounding off your answers to 3 sf.

    a $\cos 52°$ **b** $\cos 46°$ **c** $\cos 76.3°$ **d** $\cos 90°$

3 **a** Calculate $(\sin 52°)^2 + (\cos 52°)^2$ **b** Calculate $(\sin 46°)^2 + (\cos 46°)^2$

    c Calculate $(\sin 76.3°)^2 + (\cos 76.3°)^2$ **d** Calculate $(\sin 90°)^2 + (\cos 90°)^2$

    e What do you notice about your answers?

4 Use your calculator to work out the value of

    a $\tan 52°$ **b** $\tan 46°$ **c** $\tan 76.3°$

5 Use your calculator to work out the value of

    a $\sin 52° \div \cos 52°$ **b** $\sin 46° \div \cos 46°$ **c** $\sin 76.3° \div \cos 76.3°$

    d What connects your answers with the answers to Question **4**?

6 Use your calculator to work out the value of

    a $6 \sin 55°$ **b** $7 \cos 45°$ **c** $13 \sin 67°$ **d** $20 \cos 38°$

7 Use your calculator to work out the value of

    a $\dfrac{6}{\sin 55°}$ **b** $\dfrac{7}{\cos 45°}$ **c** $\dfrac{13}{\sin 67°}$ **d** $\dfrac{20}{\cos 38°}$

8 Using the following triangle, calculate sin and cos for the angle marked x. Leave your answers as fractions.

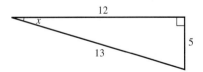

★9 You are given that $\sin x = \dfrac{5}{\sqrt{34}}$. Work out the value of $\cos x$.

Use your calculator to find the answers to the following. Give your answers to 1 dp.

1 What angles have sines of
  a 0.4   **b** 0.707   **c** 0.879   **d** 0.666666666666666…

2 What angles have cosines of
  a 0.4   **b** 0.707   **c** 0.879   **d** 0.333333333333333…

3 What angles have sines of
  a $3 \div 8$ **b** $1 \div 3$ **c** $3 \div 10$ **d** $5 \div 8$

4 What angles have cosines of
  a $3 \div 8$ **b** $1 \div 3$ **c** $3 \div 10$ **d** $5 \div 8$

 5 You are given that sin 54° = 0.809 to 3 dp. What angle has a cosine of 0.809?

1 Draw five right-angled triangles with different side lengths, but each with an angle on the base of 30° as shown below.

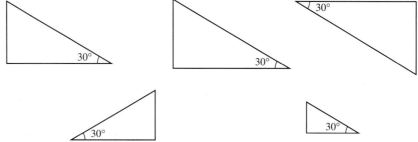

2 Measure the sides as accurately as you can. Then label the side facing the 30° as 'Opposite', and the side next to both the right-angle and the 30°, as 'Adjacent'.

3 For each triangle, calculate to 2 decimal places the value of $\dfrac{\text{Opposite}}{\text{Adjacent}}$.

4 Use your calculator to check that tan 30° is 0.577 (3sf).

5 You should notice that the average figure you have for $\dfrac{\text{Opposite}}{\text{Adjacent}}$ is the same as tan 30°.

6 See if this happens for angles other than 30° in a right-angled triangle.

Use your calculator to find these results, rounding off the display to 3 sf.

1 **a** sin 64°   **b** cos 17°   **c** tan 56.3°   **d** sin 79°   **e** cos 26°
    f tan 49°   **g** sin 37°   **h** cos 14°   **i** tan 46°   **j** sin 82°

2
a 4 tan 74°   **b** 5 tan 51°   **c** 11 tan 26°   **d** 4 tan 87°   **e** 7 tan 18°
f 6 sin 9°   **g** 11 cos 64°   **h** 8 sin 21°   **i** 3 cos 26°   **j** 7 sin 35°

3
a $\dfrac{7}{\tan 39°}$ **b** $\dfrac{6}{\sin 28°}$ **c** $\dfrac{8}{\cos 82°}$ **d** $\dfrac{2}{\tan 62°}$ **e** $\dfrac{4}{\sin 59°}$

4
a tan 46°   **b** sin 71°   **c** cos 63°   **d** tan 87°   **e** cos 62°
f sin 34°   **g** tan 73°   **h** cos 41°   **i** sin 61°   **j** tan 28°

5
a 5 tan 47°   **b** 8 tan 15°   **c** 16 tan 67°   **d** 9 tan 77°   **e** 8 tan 27°
f 5 sin 39°   **g** 21 cos 43°   **h** 9 sin 56°   **i** 4 cos 67°   **j** 8 sin 53°

6
a $\dfrac{9}{\tan 83°}$ **b** $\dfrac{7}{\sin 71°}$ **c** $\dfrac{6}{\cos 29°}$ **d** $\dfrac{1}{\tan 16°}$ **e** $\dfrac{5}{\sin 81°}$

HOMEWORK 18E

1 Find the value marked x in each of these diagrams.

a
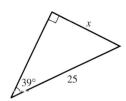

b
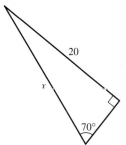

c

d
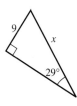

e
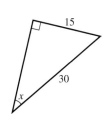

f
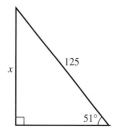

2 Angle θ has a sine of $\frac{7}{20}$. Calculate the missing lengths in these triangles.

a

b
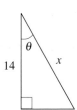

c
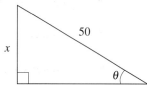

★3 Caxton is due north of Ashville and due west of
    Peaton. A pilot flies directly from Ashville to Peaton,
    a distance of 15 km, on a bearing of 050°.
    a Calculate the direct distance from Caxton to
         Peaton.
    b Find the bearing of Ashville from Peaton.

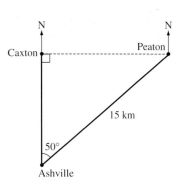

HOMEWORK 18F

1 Find the value marked x in each of these triangles.

a

b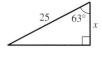

c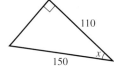

d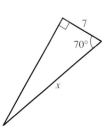

e

f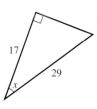

 2 Angle θ has a cosine of $\frac{7}{15}$. Calculate the missing lengths in these triangles.

a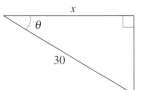

b

c

★3 The diagram shows the positions of three
    telephone masts A, B and C.
    Mast C is 6 kilometres due east of Mast B.
    Mast A is due north of Mast B, and 9 kilometres
    from Mast C.
    a Calculate the distance of A from B. Give your
         answer in kilometres, correct to 3 sf.
    b Calculate the size of the angle marked $x°$. Give
         your angle correct to 1 dp.

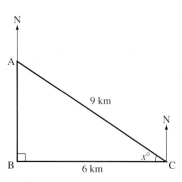

1   Find the value marked x in each of these triangles.

a
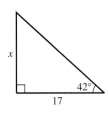

b
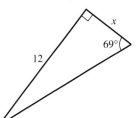

c
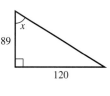

d
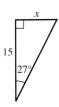

e
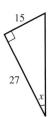

f
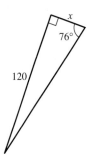

 2   Angle θ has a tangent of $\frac{2}{3}$. Calculate the missing lengths in these triangles.

a
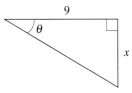

b
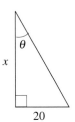

c
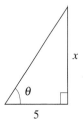

★3   The sensor for a security light is fixed to a house wall 2.25 m above the ground. It can detect movement on the ground up to 15 m away from the house. B is the furthest point where the sensor, A, can detect movement. Calculate the size of angle x.

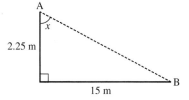

1   Find the angle or length marked x in each of these triangles.

a

b
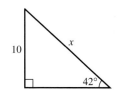

c
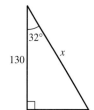

d

e

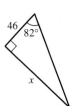

f

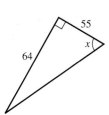

g

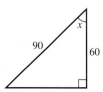

h

i

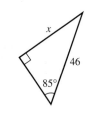

✗ ★2 The diagram shows a right-angled triangle, ABC.
Angle C = 90° and AB = 10 cm.
Given that cos B = 0.8, sin B = 0.6 and tan B = 0.75,
calculate the length of AC.

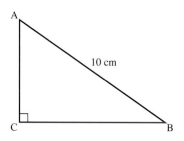

3 A lift at the seaside takes people from sea level to
the top of a cliff, as shown. From sea level to the
top of the cliff, the lift travels 23 m and rises a
height of 21 m.
a Calculate the distance AC. Give your answer
to an appropriate degree of accuracy.
b Calculate angle BCA.

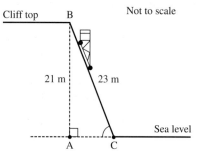

✎ HOMEWORK 18 I

1 A ladder 8 m long rests against a wall. The foot of the ladder is 2.7 m from the base of the
wall. What angle does the ladder make with the ground?

2 The ladder in Question **1** has a 'safe angle' with the ground of between 70° and 80°.
What are the safe limits for the distance of the foot of the ladder from the wall?

3 Angela walks 60 m from the base of a block of flats
and then measures the angle from the ground to the
top of the flats to be 42° as shown in the diagram.
How high is the block of flats?

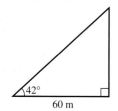

4 A slide is at an angle of 46° to the horizontal. The slide is 7 metres long. How high is the top of the slide above the ground?

5 Use trigonometry to calculate the angle that the diagonal makes with the long side of a rectangle 9 cm by 5 cm.

★6 The diagram shows the end view of a building. BCD is a right-angled triangle. Angle BCD = 90°. BC = 5 m and BD = 9.5 m.

   a Calculate angle CBD.

CH is perpendicular to AE.

AB = ED = 3.5 m.

   b Calculate CH, the height of the building.

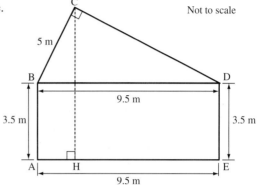

Not to scale

HOMEWORK 18J

1 Eric sees an aircraft in the sky. The aircraft is at a horizontal distance of 15 km from Eric. The angle of elevation is 42°. How high is the aircraft?

2 A man standing 100 m from the base of a block of flats looks at the top of it and notices that the angle of elevation of the top is 49°. How high are the flats?

3 A man stands 15 metres from a tree. The angle of elevation of the top of the tree from his eye is 25°. If his eye is 1.5 metres above the ground, how high is the tree?

4 A bird, sat on the very top of the tree in Question **3**, sees a worm just by the foot of the man. What is the angle of depression from the bird's eye to the worm?

5 I walk 200 metres away from a chimney that is 120 metres high. What is the angle of elevation from my eye to the top of the chimney? (Ignore the height of eye above ground).

6 If you are now told that the height of the eye in Question **5** was 1.8 metres above ground, how much different is the angle of elevation?

★7 A boat B is moored 50 m from the foot of a vertical cliff. The angle of depression of the boat from the top of the cliff is 52°.

   a Calculate the height of the cliff.

   b The boat is released from its mooring and it drifts 350 m directly away from the cliff. Calculate the angle of elevation of the top of the cliff from the boat.

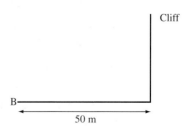

1 **a** A ship sails for 85 km on a bearing of 067°. How far east has it travelled?
   b How far north has the ship sailed?

2 Rotherham is 11 miles south of Barnsley and 2 miles west of Barnsley. What is the bearing of
   a Barnsley from Rotherham   **b** Rotherham from Barnsley?

3 A plane sets off from airport A and flies due east for 100 km, then turns to fly due south for 80 km before landing at an airport B. What is the bearing of airport B from airport A?

4 Mountain A is due east of a walker. Mountain B is due south of the walker. The guidebook says that mountain A is 5 km from mountain B, on a bearing of 038°. How far is the walker from mountain B?

5 The diagram shows the relative distances and bearings of three ships A, B and C.
   a How far north of A is B? (Distance x on diagram.)
   b How far north of B is C? (Distance y on diagram.)
   c How far west of A is C? (Distance z on diagram.)
   d What is the bearing of A from C? (Angle $w°$ on diagram.)

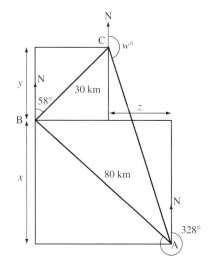

★6 An aeroplane is flying from Leeds (L) to London Heathrow (H). It flies 150 miles on a bearing 136° to point A. It then turns through 90° and flies the final 80 miles to H.
   a **i** Show clearly why the angle marked x is equal to 46°.
      ii Give the bearing of H from A.
   b Use Pythagoras' theorem to calculate the distance LH.
   c **i** Calculate the size of the angle marked y.
      ii Work out the bearing of L from H.

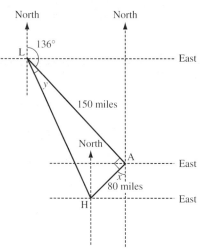

HOMEWORK 18L

In Questions **1** and **2**, find the side or angle marked *x*.

1

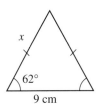

2

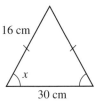

3 This diagram below shows a roof truss.
How wide is the roof?

4 Calculate the area of each of these triangles.

a

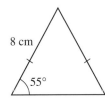

b

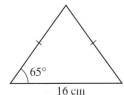

★5 An isosceles triangle has two sides of 12 cm and an angle of 62°. Calculate both possible areas.

Chapter 19   Units

HOMEWORK 19A

Decide in which metric unit you would most likely measure each of the following amounts.

1 The height of your best friend.

2 The distance from School to your home.

3 The thickness of a CD.

4 The weight of your maths teacher.

5 The amount of water in a lake.

6 The weight of a slice of bread.

7 The length of a double decker bus.

8 The weight of a kitten.

Estimate the approximate metric length, weight or capacity of each of the following.

9 This book (both length and weight).

10 The length of the road you live on. (You do not need to walk along it all.)

11 The capacity of a bottle of wine (metric measure).

12 A door (length, width and weight).

13 The diameter of a £1 coin, and its weight.

14 The distance from your school to The Houses of Parliamant (London).

HOMEWORK 19B

Length	10 mm = 1 cm, 1000 mm = 100 cm = 1 m, 1000 m = 1 km
Weight	1000 gm = 1 kg , 1000 kg = 1 t
Capacity	10 ml = 1 cl, 1000 ml = 100 cl = 1 litre
Volume	1000 litres = 1 m^3, 1 ml = 1 cm^3

Fill in the gaps using the information above.

1 155 cm = ... m

2 95 mm = ... cm

3 780 mm = ... m

4 3100 m = ... km

5 310 cm = ... m

6 3050 mm = ... m

7 156 mm = ... cm

8 2180 m = ... km

9 1070 mm = ... m

10 1324 cm = ... m

11 175 m = ... km

12 83 mm = ... m

13 620 mm = ... cm

14 2130 cm = ... m

15 5120 m = ... km

16 8150 g = ... kg

17 2300 kg = ... t

18 32 ml = ... cl

19 1360 ml = ... l

20 580 cl = ... l

21 950 kg = ... t

22 120 g = ... kg

23 150 ml = ... l

24 350 cl = ... l

25 540 ml = ... cl

26 2060 kg = ... t

27 7500 ml = ... l

28 3800 g = ... kg

29 605 cl = ... l

30 15 ml = ... l

31 6300 l = ... m^3

32 45 ml = ... cm^3

33 2350 l = ... m^3

34 720 l = ... m^3

35 8.2 m = ... cm

36 71 km = ... m

37 8.6 m = ... mm

38 15.6 cm = ... mm

39 0.83 m = ... cm

40 5.15 km = ... m

41 1.85 cm = ... mm

42 2.75 m = ... cm

HOMEWORK 19C

Length	12 inches = 1 foot, 3 feet = 1 yard, 1760 yards = 1 mile
Weight	16 ounces = 1 pound, 14 pounds = 1 stone, 2240 pounds = 1 ton
Capacity	8 pints = 1 gallon

Fill in the gaps using the information above.

1 5 feet = ... inches

2 5 yards = ... feet

3 3 miles = ... yards

4 6 pounds = ... ounces

5 5 stones = ... pounds

6 2 tons = ... pounds

7 4 gallons = ... pints

8 7 feet = ... inches

9 2 yards = ... inches

10 11 yards = ... feet

11 5 pounds = ... ounces

12 72 inches = ... feet

13 6 stones = ... pounds

14 39 feet = ... yards

15 2 stones = ... ounces

16 4400 yards = ... miles

17 12 gallons = ... pints

18 2 miles = ... feet

19 84 inches = ... feet

20 105 pounds = ... stones

21 48 pints = ... gallons

22 48 ounces = ... pounds

23 21 feet = ... yards

24 22 400 pounds = ... tons

25 2 miles = ... inches

26 256 ounces = ... pounds

27 80 pints = ... gallons

28 280 pounds = ... stones

29 31 680 feet = ... miles

30 2 tons = ... ounces

HOMEWORK 19D

Remember:

Length	1 inch ≈ 2.5 centimetres		
	1 mile ≈ 1.61 kilometres	or	5 miles ≈ 8 kilometres
Weight	1 pound ≈ 450 grams	or	2.2 pounds ≈ 1 kilogram
Capacity	1 pint ≈ 570 millilitres	or	1 gallon ≈ 4.5 litres

Complete the gaps using the conversions above.

1 9 inches ≈ ____ cm

2 8 kg ≈ ____ pounds

3 40 miles ≈ ____ km

4 13 gallons ≈ ____ litres

5 15 pints ≈ ____ m*l*

6 55 litres ≈ ____ gallons

7 25 cm ≈ ____ inches

8 60 km ≈ ____ miles

9 32 pounds ≈ ____ kg

10 1800 m*l* ≈ ____ pints

11 150 miles ≈ ____ km

12 80 inches ≈ ____ cm

13 64 kg ≈ ____ pounds

14 30 gallons ≈ ____ litres

15 12 pints ≈ ____ m*l*

16 120 km ≈ ____ miles

17 150 pounds ≈ ____ kg

18 50 cm ≈ ____ inches

19 22 km ≈ ____ miles

20 120 litres ≈ ____ gallons

21 3 gallons ≈ ____ m*l*

22 2500 m*l* ≈ ____ pints

23 12 inches ≈ ____ cm

24 14 pounds ≈ ____ kg

25 15 litres ≈ ____ gallons

26 1 tonne ≈ ____ pounds

27 36 inches ≈ ____ cm

28 28 000 m ≈ ____ inches

29 2240 pounds ≈ ____ kg

30 72 inches ≈ ____ m

HOMEWORK 19E

Use these exchange rates to convert one currency to another.

1 £60 to $

2 £90 to DM

3 £200 to €

4 £270 to BFr

5 £140 to SKr

6 £340 to ¥

7 £650 to SFr

8 £1300 to L

9 DM 186 to £

10 SFr 380 to £

11 BFr 470 to £

12 ¥480 to £

13 L 42 000 to £

14 £85 to L

15 € 230 to £

16 FFr 340 to £

17 £180 to $

18 SFR 630 to £

19 £580 to BFr

20 L 2 million to £

21 $283 to £

22 ¥40 to £

23 £75 to SKr

24 € 109 to £

Exchange Rates for £1	
US Dollar	$1.512
European currency unit	€ 1.423
German deutschmark	DM 3.351
Italian lira	L 3317.35
Japenese yen	¥187.53
Swedish krona	SKr 15.869
Swiss franc	SFr 2.617
French franc	FFr 11.238
Belgian franc	BFr 69.115

25	£800 to SFr	26	$500 to DM	27	SFr 720 to £	28	£370 to €
29	DM 60 to $	30	FFr235 to $	31	SKr 85 to $	32	¥380 to $
33	$560 to €	34	¥520 to €	35	DM 740 to €	36	L 640 to $
37	BFr 580 to DM	38	L 60 000 to DM	39	Y820 to DM	40	SFr 500 to DM
41	¥280 to FFr	42	SKr 460 to FFr	43	L900 000 to FFr	44	BFr 9356 to FFr

Q HOMEWORK 19F

1 Compare the following pairs of products and state which is the better buy and why.

a Earl Grey Tea: a small tin which is 250 g for £1.40 or a large packet which is 600 g for £3.10.

b Peas: a 120 g tin at 15p or a 500 g tin at 49p.

c Sugar: a small 650 g bag at 62p or a 1 kg bag at 96p.

d Chocolate sauce: a medium tube which is 95 ml for 99p or a large tube which is 220 ml for £1.90.

e Corn Flakes: a large box which is 800 g for £1.80 or a medium box which is 550 g for £1.25.

f Digestive biscuits: a medium pack which is 260 g for 98p or a large pack which is 350g for £1.32.

g Single cream: a small tub which is 100 ml for 38p or a large tub which is 240 ml for 72p.

2 Mandy wants to buy some sun tan oil. In the local chemist she sees the following bottles.

Small bottle   175 ml at a cost of £1.68
Medium bottle   250 ml at a cost of £2.35
Large bottle   800 ml at a cost of £6.75

a Which bottle is offered at the cheapest cost per litre?

When Mandy sunbathes all day, she will use about 100 ml of sun tan oil a day.

b She is on a holiday abroad for 15 days. What is the cheapest way in which she can buy just enough sun tan oil for the holiday?

Chapter 20   Loci and angles in a circle

Q HOMEWORK 20A

1 A is a fixed point. Sketch the locus of the point P when AP > 3 cm and AP < 6 cm.

2 A and B are two fixed points 4 cm apart. Sketch the locus of the point P for the following situations:

a AP < BP   **b** P is always within 3 cm of A and within 2 cm of B.

3 A fly is tethered by a length of spider's web that is 1 m long. Describe the locus that the fly can still buzz about in.

4 ABC is an equilateral triangle of side 4 cm. In each of the following loci, the point P moves only inside the triangle. Sketch the locus in each case.

a AP = BP   **b** AP < BP
c CP < 2 cm   **d** CP > 3 cm and BP > 3 cm

5 A wheel rolls around the inside of a square. Sketch the locus of the centre of the wheel.

6 The same wheel rolls around the outside of the square. Sketch the locus of the centre of the wheel.

★7 Two ships A and B, which are 7 km apart, both hear a distress signal from a fishing boat. The fishing boat is less than 4 km from ship A and is less than 4.5 km from ship B. A helicopter pilot sees that the fishing boat is nearer to ship A than to ship B. Use accurate construction to show the region which contains the fishing boat. Shade this region.

HOMEWORK 20B

For questions 1 to 3, you should start by sketching the picture given in each question on a 6 × 6 grid, each square of which is 1 cm by 1 cm. The scale for each question is given.

1 A goat is tethered by a rope, 10 m long, and a stake that is 2 m from each side of a field. What is the locus of the area that the goat can graze? Use a scale of 1 cm : 2 m.

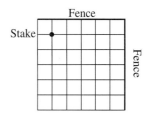

2 A cow is tethered to a rail at the top of a fence 4 m long. The rope is 4 m long. Sketch the area that the cow can graze. Use a scale of 1 cm : 2 m.

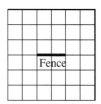

3 A horse is tethered to a corner of a shed, 3 m by 1 m. The rope is 4 m long. Sketch the area that the horse can graze. Use a scale of 1 cm : 1 m.

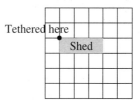

For questions 4 to 6, you should use a copy of the map on page 78. For each question, trace the map and mark on those points that are relevant to that question.

4 A radio station broadcasts from Birmingham with a range that is just far enough to reach York. Another radio station broadcasts from Glasgow with a range that is just far enough to reach Newcastle.

  a Sketch the area to which each station can broadcast.

  b Will the Birmingham station broadcast as far as Norwich?

  c Will they then interfere with each other?

5 An air traffic control centre is to be built in Newcastle. If it has a range of 200 km, will it cover all the area of Britain North of Sheffield and South of Glasgow?

6 A radio transmitter is to be built so that it is the same distance from Exeter, Norwich and Newcastle.

  a Draw the perpendicular bisectors of the lines joining these three places to find where the station is to be built.

  b Birmingham has so many radio stations that it cannot have another one within 50 km. Can the transmitter be built?

1   Find the value of *x* in each of these circles with centre O.

a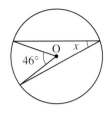

b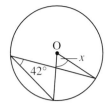

c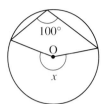

d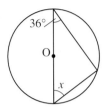

e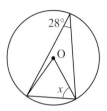

f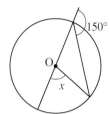

2   Find the value of *x* in each of these circles.

a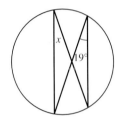

b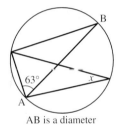

AB is a diameter

c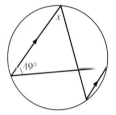

3   In the diagram, O is the centre of the circle. Find

   a   ∠EDF

   b   ∠DEG

   c   ∠EGF

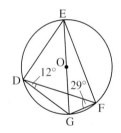

4   Find the values of *x* and *y* in each of these circles. O is the centre.

a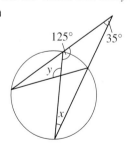

b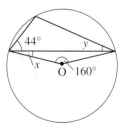

PROOF   5   ABCD are points on a circle. AB is parallel to CD.
Prove that ∠BAD = ∠ADC

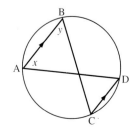

★**6** In each diagram, O is the centre of a circle.

   a Calculate the value of angle *a*.   **b** Calculate the value of angle *b*.

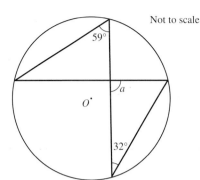

Not to scale

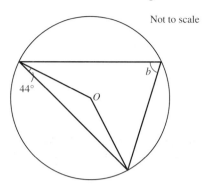

Not to scale

◯ HOMEWORK 20D

1 Find the size of the lettered angles in each of these circles.

  a

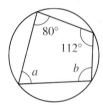

  b

  c

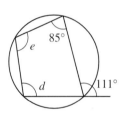

  d

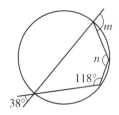

2 Find the values of *x* and *y* in each of these circles.

  a

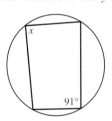

  b

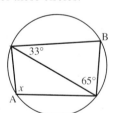

  c

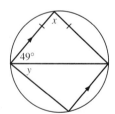

3 Find the values of *x* and *y* in each of these circles, centre O.

  a

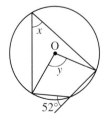

  b

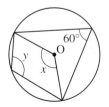

  c

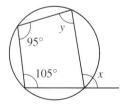

★**4** ABCD are points on a circle. AB is parallel to CD.
Prove that $\angle BAC = \angle ABD$

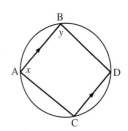

1 In each diagram, TP and TQ are tangents to a circle, centre O. Find values for r and x.

a

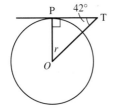

b

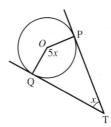

2 Each diagram shows a tangent to a circle, centre O. Find each value of y.

a

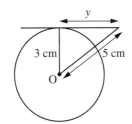

b

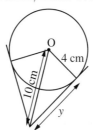

3 Each diagram shows a tangent to a circle, centre O. Find x and y in each case.

a

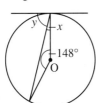

b

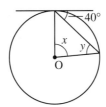

4 In each of the diagrams, TP and TQ are tangents to the circle, centre O. Find each value of x.

a

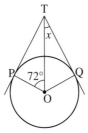

b

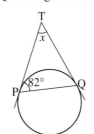

★5 In the diagram, AB = AD
and angle ADB = 69°.

  a Work out the size of angle BED. Give
    reasons for each step of your working.
  b Work out the size of angle BCD

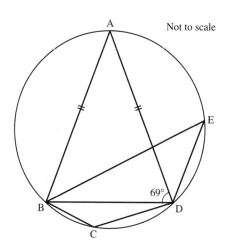

Not to scale

Chapter 21   Graphs 2

 HOMEWORK 21A

1 Draw the graph of $y = x + 1$.

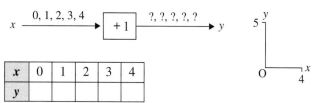

x	0	1	2	3	4
y					

2 Draw the graph of $y = 2x + 1$.

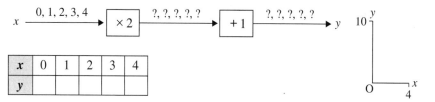

x	0	1	2	3	4
y					

3 Draw the graph of $y = 3x + 1$.

x	0	1	2	3	4
y					

4 Draw the graph of $y = x - 1$.

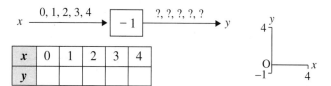

x	0	1	2	3	4
y					

★5 **a** Draw the graphs of $y = x - 2$ and $y = 2x - 1$ on the same grid.

   b Where do the graphs cross?

★6 **a** Draw the graphs of $y = 2x$ and $y = x + 2$ on the same grid.

   b Where do the graphs cross?

◯ HOMEWORK 21B

Draw the graph for each of the equations given.

Follow these hints.

● Use the highest and smallest values of x given as your range.

● When the first part of the function is a division, pick x-values that divide exactly to avoid fractions.

● Always label your graphs. This is particularly important when you are drawing two graphs on the same set of axes.

● Create a table of values. You will often have to complete these in your examinations.

1 Draw the graph of $y = 2x + 3$ for x-values from 0 to 5 ($0 \leq x \leq 5$).

2 Draw the graph of $y = 3x - 1$ ($0 \leq x \leq 5$)

3 Draw the graph of $y = \dfrac{x}{2} - 2$ ($0 \leq x \leq 12$)

4 Draw the graph of $y = 2x + 1$ ($-2 \leq x \leq 2$)

5 Draw the graph of $y = \dfrac{x}{2} + 5$ ($-6 \leq x \leq 6$)

6 **a** On the same set of axes, draw the graphs of
     $y = 3x - 1$ and $y = 2x + 3$ ($0 \leq x \leq 5$)

   b Where do the two graphs cross?

7 **a** On the same axes, draw the graphs of
     $y = 4x - 3$ and $y = 3x + 2$ ($0 \leq x \leq 6$)

   b Where do the two graphs cross?

8 **a** On the same axes, draw the graphs of
     $y = \dfrac{x}{2} + 1$ and $y = \dfrac{x}{3} + 2$ ($0 \leq x \leq 12$)

   b Where do the two graphs cross?

9 **a** On the same axes, draw the graphs of
     $y = 2x + 3$ and $y = 2x - 1$ ($0 \leq x \leq 4$)

   b Do the graphs cross? If not, why not?

10 **a** Copy and complete the table to draw the graph of
     $x + y = 6$ ($0 \leq x \leq 6$)

   b Now draw the graph of $x + y = 3$

x	0	1	2	3	4	5	6
y							

1 Find the gradient of each of these lines.

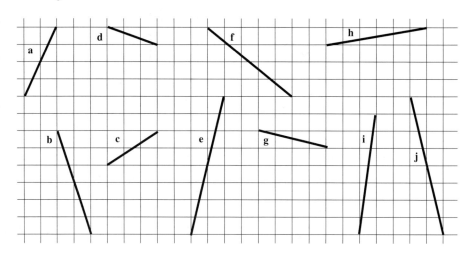

2 Draw lines with gradients of

    a 3   **b** $\frac{1}{2}$ **c** −1   **d** 8   **e** $\frac{3}{4}$ **f** $-\frac{1}{3}$

3 **a** Draw a pair of axes with both x and y showing from −10 to 10

    b Draw on the grid, lines with the following gradients; start each line at the origin. Clearly label each line.

       i $\frac{1}{2}$ **ii** 1   **iii** 2   **iv** 4   **v** −4   **vi** −2   **vii** −1   **viii** $-\frac{1}{2}$

    c Describe the symmetries of your diagram.

1 Draw these lines using the gradient-intercept method. Use the same grid, taking both x and y from −10 to 10. If the grid gets too 'crowded', draw another one.

    a $y = 2x + 4$ **b** $y = 3x − 2$ **c** $y = \frac{1}{2}x + 1$ **d** $y = x + 5$

    e $y = 4x − 1$ **f** $y = 2x − 5$ **g** $y = \frac{1}{4}x − 1$ **h** $y = x − 1$

    i $y = 6x − 2$ **j** $y = x + 3$ **k** $y = \frac{3}{4}x − 2$ **l** $y = 3x − 4$

For the next questions, use grids showing x, from −6 to 6, and y, from −8 to 8.

2 **a** Using the gradient-intercept method, draw the following lines on the same grid.

       i $y = 3x + 2$ **ii** $y = 2x − 1$

    b Where do the lines cross?

3 **a** Using the gradient-intercept method, draw the following lines on the same grid.

       i $y = x + 2$ **ii** $y = 5x$

    b Where do the lines cross?

1 Give the equation of each of these lines.

a 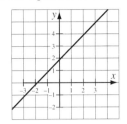 **b** 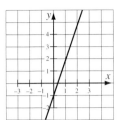 **c**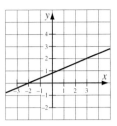

2 In each of these grids, there are two lines.

a 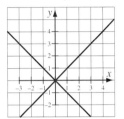 **b** 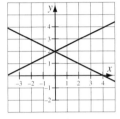 **c**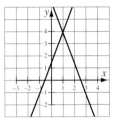

i Find the equation of each line.

ii Describe any symmetries you see about the two lines.

3 The diagram shows four lines crossing to create a rectangle. Write down the equation of each of the four lines.

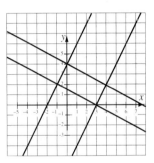

1 Draw these lines using the cover-up method. Use the same grid, taking x from -10 to 10 and y from -10 to 10. If the grid gets too 'crowded', draw another.

a $2x + 3y = 6$ **b** $3x + 4y = 12$ **c** $5x - 4y = 20$ **d** $x + y = 8$

e $2x - 3y = 18$ **f** $x - y = 6$ **g** $3x - 5y = 15$ **h** $3x - 2y = 12$

i $5x + 4y = 30$ **j** $x + y = -1$ **k** $x + y = 5$ **l** $x - y = -6$

2 a Using the cover-up method, draw the following lines on the same grid.

i $x + 2y = 4$ **ii** $2x - y = 2$

b Where do the lines cross?

3 a Using the cover-up method, draw the following lines on the same grid.

i $x + 2y = 6$ **ii** $2x - y = 2$

b Where do the lines cross?

By drawing their graphs, find the solution of each of these pairs of simultaneous equations.

1 $x + 4y = 1$
   $x - y = 6$

2 $y = 2x + 1$
   $3x + 2y = 23$

3 $y = 2x + 5$
   $y = x + 4$

4 $y = x$
   $x - y = 4$

5 $y + 10 = 2x$
   $5x + y = 18$

6 $y = 5x - 1$
   $y = 3x + 2$

7 $y = x + 11$
   $x + y = 5$

8 $y - 3x = 8$
   $y = x + 6$

9 $y = -x$
   $y = 4x + 15$

10 $3x + 2y = 2$
   $y = -2x$

11 $y = 3x - 4$
   $y + x = 6$

12 $y = 3x - 12$
   $x + y = 2$

For all the axes in this exercise, take x from -10 to 10.

1 **a** Draw the line $x = 3$ (as a solid line).
   b Shade the region defined as $x \leq 3$.

2 **a** Draw the line $x = -2$ (as a solid line).
   b Shade the region defined as $x < -2$.

3 **a** Draw the line $x = -3$ (as a solid line).
   b Draw the line $x = 2$ (as a solid line).
   c Shade the region defined as $-3 \leq x \leq 2$.

4 **a** Draw the line $y = -2$ (as a solid line).
   b Draw the line $y = 1$ (as a solid line).
   c Shade the region defined as $-2 \leq y \leq 1$.

5 **a** On the same grid, draw the regions defined by the inequalities
      i $-3 \leq x \leq 2$ **ii** $-2 \leq y \leq 2$
   b Are the following points in the region defined by both inequalities?
      i $(1, 1)$ **ii** $(-2, 2)$ **iii** $(1, 4)$

6 **a** Draw the line $x = 3x - 1$ (as a solid line).
   b Shade the region defined as $x \leq 3x - 1$.

HOMEWORK 22A

1 The table shows the heights and
weights of twelve students in a class.

    a Plot the data on a scatter diagram.

    b Draw the line of best fit.

    c Jayne was absent from the class,
but they knew she was 132 cm tall.
Use the line of best fit to estimate
her weight.

    d A new girl joined the class who
weighed 55 kg. What height would
you expect her to be?

Student	Weight (kg)	Height (cm)
Ann	51	123
Bridie	58	125
Ciri	57.5	127
Di	62	128
Emma	59.5	129
Flo	65	129
Gill	65	133
Hanna	65.5	135
Ivy	71	137
Joy	75.5	140
Keri	70	143
Laura	78	145

★2 The table shows the marks for ten pupils
in their mathematics and music examinations.

    a Plot the data on a scatter diagram. Take
the x-axis for the mathematics scores and
mark it from 20 to 100. Take the y-axis
for the music scores and mark it from 20
to 100.

    b Draw the line of best fit.

    c One of the pupils was ill when they took
the music examination. Which pupil
was it most likely to be?

    d Another pupil, Kris, was absent for the
music examination but scored 45 in
mathematics, what mark would you
expect him to have got in music?

    e Another pupil, Lex, was absent for the
mathematics examination but scored 78
in music, what mark would you expect
him to have got in mathematics?

Pupil	Maths	Music
Alex	52	50
Ben	42	52
Chris	65	60
Don	60	59
Ellie	77	61
Fan	83	74
Gary	78	64
Hazel	87	68
Irene	29	26
Jez	53	45

1 **a** Plot the line graph of the bills shown in the table, and on the same axes plot a four-quarters moving average.

	1997	**1998**	**1999**	**2000**
1st quarter	£102	£98	£106	£111
2nd quarter	£87	£92	£96	£98
3rd quarter	£66	£56	£81	£93
4th quarter	£81	£106	£105	£109

b Comment on these bills over the four years.

2 The table shows the attendances at a theatre to the nearest hundred during one month.

	Mon	**Tue**	**Wed**	**Thu**	**Fri**	**Sat**	**Sun**
1st week	11	20	31	32	38	42	31
2nd week	11	12	27	24	24	42	28
3rd week	8	12	24	26	26	39	28
4th week	8	15	24	20	20	40	27

a Plot a line graph of the attendances, and also plot a seven-days moving average.
b Comment on the trend in the attendances?

3 A company making dishwashers has the following sales figures (in hundreds).

	Jan	**Feb**	**Mar**	**Apr**	**May**	**Jun**	**Jul**	**Aug**	**Sep**	**Oct**	**Nov**	**Dec**
1999	24	27	24	28	27	7	31	24	28	26	28	24
2000	27	28	24	28	26	28	27	27	31	31	23	28

a Plot a line graph of the sales, and a three-months moving average.
b Comment on any trends in the sales.

1 An army squad were all sent on a one mile run. Their coach recorded the times they took. This table shows the results.

a Copy the table and complete a cumulative frequency column.

b Draw a cumulative frequency diagram.

c Use your diagram to estimate the median time and the interquartile range.

Time (seconds)	Number of runners
$200 < x \le 240$	3
$240 < x \le 260$	7
$260 < x \le 280$	12
$280 < x \le 300$	23
$300 < x \le 320$	7
$320 < x \le 340$	5
$340 < x \le 360$	5

★2 A company had some web pages. They recorded how many times they were visited on one day.

Number of visits	Number of pages
$0 < x \le 50$	6
$50 < x \le 100$	9
$100 < x \le 150$	15
$150 < x \le 200$	25
$200 < x \le 250$	31
$250 < x \le 300$	37
$300 < x \le 350$	32
$350 < x \le 400$	17
$400 < x \le 450$	5

a Copy the table and complete a cumulative frequency column.

b Draw a cumulative frequency diagram.

c Use your diagram to estimate the median use of the web pages and the interquartile range.

d Pages with less than 60 visitors are going to be rewritten. About how many pages would need to be rewritten?

HOMEWORK 22D

1 The box plot below shows the number of peas in pods grown by a prize-winning gardener.

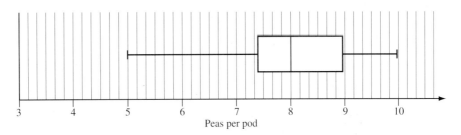

Peas per pod

A young gardener also grew some peas. These are the results for the number of peas per pod: Smallest number 3, Lower quartile 4.75, Median 5.5, Upper quartile 6.25, Biggest number 9.

a Copy the diagram and draw a box plot for the young gardener.

b Comment on the differences between the two distributions.

2 The box plot shows the monthly salaries of the men in a computer firm.

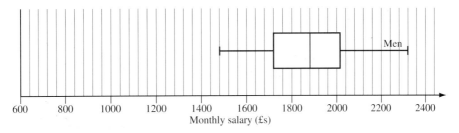

Monthly salary (£s)

The data for the women in the company is: Smallest 600, Lower quartile 1300, Median 1600, Upper Quartile 2000, Largest 2400.

a Copy the diagram and draw a box plot for the women's salaries.

b Comment on the differences between the two distributions.

3 The box plots for the hours of life of two brands of batteries are shown below.

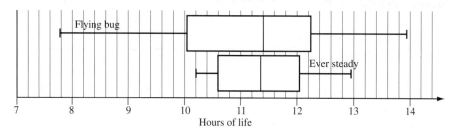

Hours of life

a Comment on the differences in the two distributions.

b Mushtaq wants to get some batteries for his palm top. Which brand would you recommend and why?

4 The following table shows some data on the times of telephone calls to two operators at a mobile phone helpline.

	Lowest time	Lowest Quartile	Medium time	Upper Quartile	Highest time
Jack	1 m 10 s	2 m 20 s	3 m 30 s	4 m 50 s	7 m 10 s
Jill	40 s	2 m 20 s	5 m 10 s	7 m 30 s	10 m 45 s

a Draw box plots to compare both sets of data.

b Comment on the differences between the distributions.

c The company has to get rid of 1 operator. Who should they get rid of and why?

★5 A school entered 80 pupils for an examination. The results are shown in the table.

Mark, x	$0 < x \leq 20$	$20 < x \leq 40$	$40 < x \leq 60$	$60 < x \leq 80$	$80 < x \leq 100$
Number of pupils	2	14	28	26	10

a Calculate an estimate of the mean.

b Complete a cumulative frequency table and draw a cumulative frequency diagram.

c **i** Use your graph to estimate the median mark.

    ii 12 of these pupils were given a grade A. Use your graph to estimate the lowest mark for which grade A was given.

d Another school also entered 80 pupils for the same examination. Their results were Lowest mark 40, Lower quartile 50, Median 60, Upper quartile 70, Highest mark 80. Draw a box plot to show these results and use it to comment on the differences between the two schools' results.

HOMEWORK 23A

1 Katrina throws two dice and records the number of doubles that she gets after various numbers of throws. The table shows her results.

Number of throws	10	20	30	50	100	200	600
Number of doubles	2	3	6	9	17	35	102

  a Calculate the experimental probability of a double at each stage that Katrina recorded her results.

  b What do you think the theoretical probability is for the number of doubles when throwing two dice?

2 Mary made a six-sided spinner, like the one shown in the diagram. She used it to play a board game with her friend Jane. The girls thought that the spinner was not very fair as it seemed to land on some numbers more than others. They threw the spinner 120 times and recorded the results. The results are shown in the table.

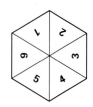

Number spinner lands on	1	2	3	4	5	6
Number of times	22	17	21	18	26	16

  a Work out the experimental probability of each number.

  b How many times would you expect each number to occur if the spinner is fair?

  c Do you think that the spinner is fair? Give a reason for your answer.

3 In a game at the fairground a player rolls a coin onto a squared board with some of the squares coloured blue, green or red. If the coin lands completely within one of the coloured squares the player wins a prize. The table below shows the probabilities of the coin landing completely within a winning colour.

Colour	Blue	Green	Red
Probability	0.3	0.2	0.1

  a On one afternoon 300 games were played. How many coins would you expect to land within   **i** a blue square   **ii** a green square   **iii** a red square?

  b What is the probability that a player loses a game?

HOMEWORK 23B

1 What is the probability of each of the following?

  a Throwing a 3 with a dice.   **b** Tossing a coin and getting a head.

  c Drawing a Jack from a pack of cards.   **d** Drawing a Club from a pack of cards.

  e Throwing a 3 or a 6 with a dice.

2 What is the probability of each of the following?

  a Throwing an odd number with a dice.

  b Throwing a square number with a dice.

  c Getting a Spade or a Diamond from a pack of cards.

  d Drawing the Jack of Diamonds from a pack of cards.

3 A bag contains 3 blue balls, 2 pink balls and 1 black ball. Joan takes a ball from the bag without looking. What is the probability that she takes out

    a a blue ball   **b** a pink ball   **c** a ball that is not black?

4 In a raffle, 800 tickets are sold. Dick has 5 tickets. What is the probability that he wins the first prize?

5 Ann, Betty, Colin, Derek, Ethel and Fiona are in the same class. Their teacher wants two pupils to do a special job.

    a Write down all the possible combinations of two people. For example, Ann and Betty, Ann and Colin (there are 15 combinations altogether).

    b How many pairs give two boys?

    c What is the probability of choosing two boys?

    d How many pairs give a boy and a girl?

    e What is the probability of choosing a boy and a girl?

    f What is the probability of choosing two girls?

6 A bag contains 12 identical tea bags. Five are Earl Grey tea and the rest are ordinary tea. I take one out and make a cup of tea with it.

    a What is the probability that I get Earl Grey tea?

    b If the first tea bag I get is Earl Grey,

       i how many Earl Grey tea bags are left

       ii how many ordinary tea bags are left?

    c After I have drunk the cup of Earl Grey tea, I pick another tea bag. What is the probability that I pick   **i** Earl Grey   **ii** ordinary tea?

7 An ordinary six-sided dice has 1 red face, 1 blue face and 4 green faces. If this dice is thrown, what is the probability that the top face will be

    a red   **b** green   **c** not blue

    d black   **e** red, green or blue?

8 Twelve-sided dice are used in adventure games. They are marked with the numbers 1 to 12. The score is the uppermost face. If a twelve-sided dice is thrown, what is the probability that the score will be

    a a number in the 3 times table   **b** a factor of 12

    c a square number   **d** a triangle number

    e a number that is not prime   **f** not a square number?

★9 Zaheda conducted a probability experiment using a packet of 40 sweets. She counted the number of sweets of each colour. Her results are shown in the table. Zaheda is going to take one sweet at random from the packet. Write down the probability

Red	Green	Orange
16	9	15

    a that Zaheda will take a green sweet from the packet

    b that the sweet Zaheda takes will **not** be red.

HOMEWORK 23C

1 Say whether these pairs of events are mutually exclusive or not.

    a Tossing two heads with two coins/tossing two tails with two coins.

    b Throwing an even number with a dice/throwing an odd number with a dice.

    c Drawing a Queen from a pack of cards/drawing an Ace from a pack of cards.

    d Drawing a Queen from a pack of cards/drawing a red card from a pack of cards.

    e Drawing a red card from a pack of cards/drawing a Heart from a pack of cards.

2 Which of the pairs of mutually exclusive events in Question **1** are also exhaustive?

3 A letter is to be chosen at random from this set of letter-cards.
M I S S I S S I P P I
    a What is the probability the letter is
       i an S   **ii** a P   **iii** a vowel?
    b Which of these pairs of events are mutually exclusive?
       i Picking an S / picking a P.   **ii** Picking an S / picking a consonant.
       iii Picking an I / picking a consonant.
    c Which pair of mutually exclusive events in part **b** is also exhaustive?

4 Two people are to be chosen for a job from this set of six people.
    Ann   Joan   Jack   John   Arthur   Ethel
    a List all of the possible pairs (there are 15 altogether).
    b What is the probability that the pair of people chosen will be
       i both female   **ii** both male   **iii** both have the same initial
       iv have different initials?
    c Which of these pairs of events are mutually exclusive?
       i Picking two women / picking two men.
       ii Picking two people of the same sex / picking two people of opposite sex.
       iii Picking two people with the same initial / picking two men.
       iv Picking two people with the same initial / picking two women.
    d Which pair of mutually exclusive events in part **c** is also exhaustive?

5 For breakfast I like to have toast, porridge or cereal. The probability I have toast is $\frac{1}{3}$, the probability I have porridge is $\frac{1}{2}$, what is the probability I have cereal?

6 A person is chosen at random. Here is a list of events.
    Event A: the person chosen is male   Event B: the person chosen is female
    Event C: the person chosen is over 18   Event D: the person chosen is under 16
    Event E: the person chosen has a degree   Event F: the person chosen is a teacher
For each of the pairs of events **i** to **x**, say whether they are
    a mutually exclusive   **b** exhaustive.
    c If they are not mutually exclusive, explain why.
       i Event A and Event B   **ii** Event A and Event C
       iii Event B and Event D   **iv** Event C and Event D
       v Event D and Event F   **vi** Event E and Event F
       vii Event E and Event D   **viii** Event A and Event E
       ix Event C and Event F   **x** Event C and Event E

★7 An amateur weather man records the weather over a year in his village. He knows that the probability of a windy day is 0.4 and that the probability of a rainy day is 0.6. Steve says 'This means it will be either rainy or windy each day as 0.4 + 0.6 = 1, which is certain.' Explain why Steve is wrong.

1 I throw an ordinary dice 600 times. How many times can I expect to get a score of 1?

2 I toss a coin 500 times. How many times can I expect to get a tail?

3 I draw a card from a pack of cards and replace it. I do this 104 times. How many times would I expect to get
  a a red card **b** a Queen **c** a red seven **d** the Jack of Diamonds?

4 The ball in a roulette wheel can land on any number from 0 to 36. I always bet on the same block of numbers 0–6. If I play all evening and there is a total of 111 spins of the wheel in that time, how many times could I expect to win?

5 I have 5 tickets for a raffle and I know that the probability of my winning the prize is 0.003. How many tickets were sold altogether in the raffle?

6 In a bag there are 20 balls, 10 of which are red, 3 yellow, and 7 blue. A ball is taken out at random and then replaced. This is repeated 200 times. How many times would I expect to get
  a a red ball **b** a yellow or blue ball
  c a ball that is not blue **d** a green ball?

7 A sampling bottle contains black and white balls. It is known that the probability of getting a black ball is 0.4. How many white balls would you expect to get in 200 samples?

8 **a** Fred is about to take his driving test. The chance he passes is $\frac{1}{3}$. His sister says 'Don't worry if you fail because you are sure to pass within three attempts because $3 \times \frac{1}{3} = 1$'. Explain why his sister is wrong.
  b If Fred does fail would you expect the chance that he passes next time to increase or decrease? Explain your answer.

★9 An opinion poll used a sample of 200 voters in one area. 112 said they would vote for Party A. There are a total of 50 000 voters in the area.
  a If they all voted, how many would you expect to vote for Party A?
  b The poll is accurate within 10%. Can Party A be confident of winning?

1 Shaheeb throws an ordinary dice. What is the probability that he throws
  a an even number **b** 5 **c** an even number or 5?

2 Jane draws a card from a pack of cards. What is the probability that she draws
  a a red card **b** a black card **c** a red or a black card?

3 Natalie draws a card from a pack of cards. What is the probability that she draws one of the following numbers?
  a Ace **b** King **c** Ace or King

4 A letter is chosen at random from the letters in the word STATISTICS. What is the probability that the letter will be
  a S **b** a vowel **c** S or a vowel?

5   A bag contains 10 white balls, 12 black balls and 8 red balls. A ball is drawn at random from the bag. What is the probability that it will be

    a   white   **b**   black   **c**   black or white

    d   not red   **e**   not red or black?

6   A spinner has numbers and colours on it, as shown in the diagram. Their probabilities are given in the tables.

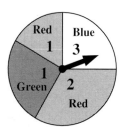

Red	0.5
Green	0.25
Blue	0.25

1	0.4
2	0.35
3	0.25

When the spinner is spun what is the probability of each of the following?

    a   Red or blue   **b**   2 or 3   **c**   3 or blue   **d**   2 or green

    e   **i**   Explain why the answer to **c** is 0.25 and not 0.5.

           ii   What is the answer to P(2 or red)?

7   Debbie has 10 CDs in her multi-changer, 4 of which are rock, 2 are dance and 4 are classical. She puts the player on random play. What is the probability that the first CD will be

    a   rock or dance   **b**   rock or classical   **c**   not rock?

8   Frank buys 1 dozen free-range eggs. The farmer tells him that a quarter of the eggs his hens lay have double yolks

    a   How many eggs with double yolks can frank expect to get?

    b   He cooks 3 and finds they all have a single yolk. He argues that he now has a 1 in 3 chance of a double yolk from the remaining eggs. Explain why he is wrong.

★9   John has a bag containing 6 red, 5 blue and 4 green balls. One ball is picked from the bag at random. What is the probability that the ball is

    a   red or blue   **b**   not blue   **c**   pink   **d**   red or not blue?

HOMEWORK 23F

1   Two dice are thrown together. Draw a probability diagram to show the total score.

    a   What is the probability of a score that is

        i 7   **ii** 5 or 8   **iii** bigger than 9   **iv** between 2 and 5

        v odd   **vi** a non-square number?

2   Two dice are thrown. Draw a probability diagram to show the outcomes as a pair of co-ordinates.

    What is the probability that

    a   the score is a 'double'

    b   at least one of the dice shows 3

    c   the score on one dice is three times the score on the other dice

    d   at least one of the dice shows an odd number

    e   both dice show a 5

    f   at least one of the dice will show a 5

    g   exactly one dice shows a 5?

3 Two dice are thrown. The score on one dice is doubled and the score on the other dice is subtracted.

Complete the probability space diagram.

For the event described above, what is the probability of a score of

a 1

b a negative number

c an even number

d 0 or 1

e a prime number?

Score on second dice						
6						6
5						
4						
3	−1					
2	0					
1	1	3	5	7	9	11
	1	2	3	4	5	6

Score on first dice

4 When two coins are tossed together, what is the probability of

    a 2 heads or 2 tails   **b** a head and a tail   **c** at least 1 head?

5 When three coins are tossed together, what is the probability of

    a 3 heads or 3 tails   **b** 2 tails and 1 head   **c** at least 1 head?

6 When a dice and a coin are thrown together, what is the probability of each of the following outcomes?

    a You get a tail on the coin and a 3 on the dice.

    b You get a head on the coin and an odd number on the dice.

★7 Max buys two bags of bulbs from his local garden centre. Each bag has 4 bulbs. Two bulbs are daffodils, one is a tulip and one is a hyacinth. Max takes one bulb from each bag.

    a There are six possible different pairs of bulbs. List them all.

    b Complete the sample space diagram.

    c What is the probability of getting two daffodil bulbs?

    d Explain why the answer is not $\frac{1}{6}$.

Hyac				HH
Tulip	DT			
Daff				
Daff	DD	DD	TD	
	Daff	**Daff**	**Tulip**	**Hyac**

HOMEWORK 23G

1 A dice is thrown twice. Copy and complete the tree diagram below to show all the outcomes.

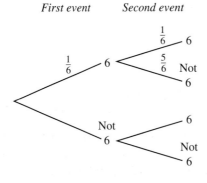

First event	Second event	Outcome	Probability
	$\frac{1}{6}$ 6	(6, 6)	$\frac{1}{6} \times \frac{1}{6} = \frac{1}{36}$
$\frac{1}{6}$ 6	$\frac{5}{6}$ Not 6	(6, Not 6)	$\frac{1}{6} \times \frac{5}{6} = \frac{5}{36}$
Not 6	6		
	Not 6		

Use your tree diagram to work out the probability of

    a getting two sixes   **b** getting one six   **c** getting no sixes.

2 A bag contains 3 red and 2 blue balls. A ball is taken out, replaced and then another ball is taken out.

   a What is the probability that the first ball taken out will be red?

   b Copy and complete the tree diagram below, showing the possible outcomes.

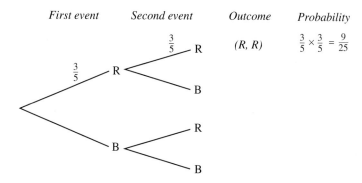

First event   *Second event*   *Outcome*   *Probability*

$$\frac{3}{5}$$ R   (R, R) $\frac{3}{5} \times \frac{3}{5} = \frac{9}{25}$

   c Using the tree diagram, what is the probability of the following outcomes?
   i 2 red balls.   **ii** Exactly 1 red ball.   **iii** At least one red ball.

3 A card is drawn from a pack of cards. It is replaced, the pack is shuffled and another card is drawn.

   a What is the probability that either card was a Spade?

   b What is the probability that either card was not a Spade?

   c Draw a tree diagram to show the outcomes of two cards being drawn as described. Use the tree diagram to work out the probability that
   i both cards will be Spades
   ii at least one of the cards will be a Spade.

4 A bag of sweets contains 5 chocolates and 4 toffees.

   I take 2 sweets out at random and eat them.

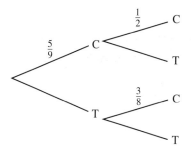

First choice   *Second choice*

   a What is the probability that the first sweet chosen is
   i a chocolate   **ii** a toffee?

   b If the first sweet chosen is a chocolate,
   i how many sweets are left to choose from
   ii how many of them are chocolates?

   c If the first sweet chosen is a toffee,
   i how many sweets are left to choose from
   ii how many of them are toffees?

   d Copy and complete the tree diagram.

   e Use the tree diagram to work out the probability that
   i both sweets will be of the same type   **ii** there is at least one chocolate chosen.

5 Thomas has to take a driving test which is in two parts. The first part is theoretical. He has a 0.4 chance of passing this. The second is practical. He has a 0.5 chance of passing this. Draw a tree diagram covering passing or failing the two parts of the test. What is the probability that he passes both parts?

6 Every Sunday morning Carol goes out for a run. She has 3 pairs of shorts of which 2 are red and 1 is blue. She has 5 T-shirts of which 3 are red and 2 are blue. Because she can't disturb her husband she gets dressed in the dark and picks a pair of shorts and a T-shirt at random.

   a What is the probability that the shorts are blue?

   b Copy and complete this tree diagram.

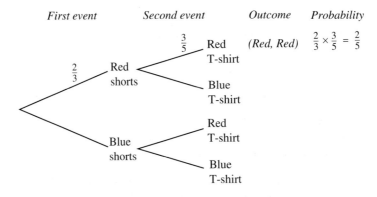

   c What is the probability that Carol goes running in

      i   a matching pair of shorts and T-shirt

      ii a mis-match of shorts and T-shirt

     iii at least one red item?

★7 Bob has a bag containing 4 blue balls, 5 red balls and 1 green ball. Sally has a bag containing 2 blue balls and 3 red balls. The balls are identical except for the colour. Bob chooses a ball at random from his bag and Sally chooses a ball at random from her bag.

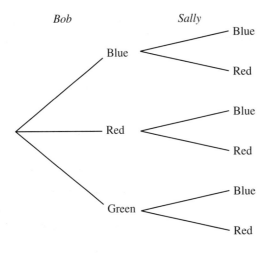

   a On a copy of the tree diagram, write the probability of each of the events on the appropriate branch.

   b Calculate the probability that both Bob and Sally will choose a blue ball.

   c Calculate the probability that the ball chosen by Bob will be a different colour from the ball chosen by Sally.

⟲ HOMEWORK 23H

1 Ahmed throws a dice twice. The dice is biased so the probability of getting a six is $\frac{1}{4}$. What is the probability that he gets

   a two sixes   **b** exactly one six?

2 Betty draws a card from a pack of cards, replaces it, shuffles the pack and then draws another card. What is the probability that the cards are
    a both Hearts   **b** a Heart and a Spade (in any order)?

3 Colin draws a card from a pack of cards, does not replace it and then draws another card. What is the probability that the cards are
    a both Hearts   **b** a Heart and a Spade (in any order)?

4 I throw a dice three times. What is the probability of getting a total score of 17 or 18?

 5 A bag contains 7 white beads and 3 black beads. I take out a bead at random, replace it and take out another bead. What is the probability that
    a both beads are black   **b** one bead is black and the other white (in any order)?

6 A bag contains 7 white beads and 3 black beads. I take out a bead at random, do not replace it and take out another bead. What is the probability that
    a both beads are black   **b** one bead is black and the other white (in any order)?

?UAM **★7** When I answer the telephone the call is never for me. Half the calls are for my daughter Janette. One-third of them are for my son Glen. The rest are for my wife Barbara.
    a I answer the telephone twice this evening. Calculate the probability that
        i the first call will be for Barbara   **ii** both calls will be for Barbara.
    b The probability that both these calls are for Janette is $\frac{1}{4}$. The probability that they are both for Glen is $\frac{1}{9}$. Calculate the probability that either they are both for Janette or both for Glen.

Chapter 24   Sequences

 HOMEWORK 24A

Look for the pattern and then write the next two lines. Check your answers with a calculator afterwards.

1
$7 \times 11 \times 13 \times 2 = 2002$
$7 \times 11 \times 13 \times 3 = 3003$
$7 \times 11 \times 13 \times 4 = 4004$
$7 \times 11 \times 13 \times 5 = 5005$

2
$3 \times 7 \times 13 \times 37 \times 2 = 20202$
$3 \times 7 \times 13 \times 37 \times 3 = 30303$
$3 \times 7 \times 13 \times 37 \times 4 = 40404$
$3 \times 7 \times 13 \times 37 \times 5 = 50505$

3
$3 \times 5 = 4^2 - 1 = 15$
$4 \times 6 = 5^2 - 1 = 24$
$5 \times 7 = 6^2 - 1 = 35$
$6 \times 8 = 7^2 - 1 = 48$

4
$3 \times 7 = 5^2 - 4 = 21$
$4 \times 8 = 6^2 - 4 = 32$
$5 \times 9 = 7^2 - 4 = 45$
$6 \times 10 = 8^2 - 4 = 60$

From your observations on the number patterns above, answer Questions **5** to **12** without using a calculator. Check with a calculator once you have attempted them.

5 $7 \times 11 \times 13 \times 9 =$ **6** $3 \times 7 \times 13 \times 37 \times 8 =$

7 $99 \times 101 =$ **8** $98 \times 102 =$

9 $7 \times 11 \times 13 \times 15 =$ **10** $3 \times 7 \times 13 \times 37 \times 15 =$

11 $998 \times 1002 =$ **12** $3 \times 7 \times 13 \times 37 \times 99 =$

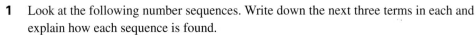

1 Look at the following number sequences. Write down the next three terms in each and explain how each sequence is found.

   a 4, 6, 8, 10, …   **b** 3, 6, 9, 12, …   **c** 2, 4, 8, 16, …

   d 5, 12, 19, 26, …   **e** 3, 30, 300, 3000, …   **f** 1, 4, 9, 16, …

2 Look carefully at each number sequence below. Find the next two numbers in the sequence and try to explain the pattern.

   a 1, 2, 3, 5, 8, 13, 21, …   **b** 2, 3, 5, 8, 12, 17, …

3 Look at the sequences below. Find the rule for each sequence and write down its next three terms.

   a 7, 14, 28, 56, …   **b** 3, 10, 17, 24, 31, …   **c** 1, 3, 7, 15, 31, …

   d 40, 39, 37, 34, …   **e** 3, 6, 11, 18, 27, …   **f** 4, 5, 7, 10, 14, 19, …

   g 4, 6, 7, 9, 10, 12, …   **h** 5, 8, 11, 14, 17, …   **i** 5, 7, 10, 14, 19, 25, …

   j 10, 9, 7, 4, …   **k** 200, 40, 8, 1.6, …   **l** 3, 1.5, 0.75, 0.375, …

1 Use each of the following rules to write down the first five terms of a sequence.

   a $3n + 1$ for $n = 1, 2, 3, 4, 5$ **b** $2n - 1$ for $n = 1, 2, 3, 4, 5$

   c $4n + 2$ for $n = 1, 2, 3, 4, 5$ **d** $2n^2$ for $n = 1, 2, 3, 4, 5$

   e $n^2 - 1$ for $n = 1, 2, 3, 4, 5$

2 Write down the first five terms of the sequence which has its nth term as

   a $n + 2$ **b** $4n - 1$ **c** $4n - 3$ **d** $n^2 + 1$ **e** $2n^2 + 1$

3 **a** Write down the first six terms of the sequence of fractions $\dfrac{2n + 1}{n + 1}$ for $n = 1, 2, 3, 4, \ldots$

     b By letting $n = 1000$ use your calculator to work out the value of the fraction as a decimal when $n = 1000$.

     c What fraction do you think the sequence is heading towards?

★4 **a** A sequence is given by $\frac{1}{2}, \frac{2}{3}, \frac{3}{4}, \frac{4}{5}, \ldots$.

       Write down

       i the 11th term of this sequence   **ii** the nth term of this sequence.

     b Each term of a second sequence is the reciprocal of the corresponding term of the sequence given in part **a**. Write down the first four terms of the second sequence.

 1 Find the nth term in each of these linear sequences.

   a 5, 7, 9, 11, 13 …   **b** 3, 7, 11, 15, 19, …   **c** 6, 11, 16, 21, 26, …

   d 3, 9, 15, 21, 27, …   **e** 4, 7, 10, 13, 16, …   **f** 3, 10, 17, 24, 31, …

2 Find the 50th term in each of these linear sequences.

   a 3, 5, 7, 9, 11, …   **b** 5, 9, 13, 17, 21, …   **c** 8, 13, 18, 23, 28, …

   d 2, 8, 14, 20, 26, …   **e** 5, 8, 11, 14, 17, …   **f** 2, 9, 16, 23, 30, …

3 For each sequence **a** to **f**, find

   i the *n*th term   **ii** the 100th term   **iii** the term closest to 100

   a 4, 7, 10, 13, 16, …   **b** 7, 9, 11, 13, 15, …   **c** 3, 8, 13, 18, 23, …

   d 1, 5, 9, 13, 17, …   **e** 2, 10, 18, 26, …   **f** 5, 6, 7, 8, 9, …

HOMEWORK 24E

1 A pattern of shapes is built up from matchsticks as shown.

  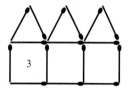

   a Draw the 4th diagram.
   b How many matchsticks are in the *n*th diagram?
   c How many matchsticks are in the 25th diagram?
   d With 200 matchsticks, which is the biggest diagram that could be made?

2 A pattern of hexagons is built up from matchsticks.

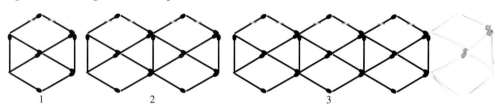

   a Draw the 4th set of hexagons in this pattern.
   b How many matchsticks are needed for the *n*th set of hexagons?
   c How many matchsticks are needed to make the 60th set of hexagons?
   d If there are only 100 matchsticks, which is the largest set of hexagons that could be made?

3 A conference centre had tables each of which could sit 3 people. When put together, the tables could seat people as shown.

 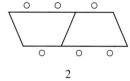 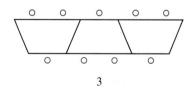

   a How many people could be seated at 4 tables?
   b How many people could be seated at *n* tables put together in this way?
   c A conference had 50 people who wished to use the tables in this way. How many tables would they need?

4 A pattern of squares is put together as shown.

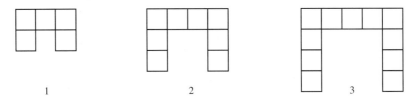

1   2   3

  a Draw the 4th diagram.

  b How many squares are in the nth diagram?

  c How many squares are in the 50th diagram?

  d With 300 squares, work out the number of the biggest diagram that could be made.

★5 Sheep enclosures are built using fences and posts.

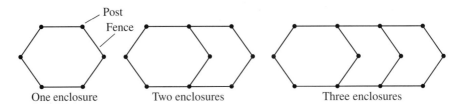

One enclosure   Two enclosures   Three enclosures

  a **i** Sketch four enclosures in a row.   **ii** Sketch five enclosures in a row.

  b Copy and complete the table below.

Number of enclosures	1	2	3	4	5	6	7	8
Number of posts	6	9	12					

  c Work out the number of posts needed for 20 enclosures in a row.

  d Write down an expression to find the number of posts needed for n enclosures in a row.

HOMEWORK 24F

1 For each of the sequences **a** to **e**
  i write down the next two terms   **ii** find the nth term.

  a 1, 4, 9, 16, 25, …   **b** 2, 5, 10, 17, 26, …   **c** 5, 8, 13, 20, 29, …

  d 2, 8, 18, 32, 50, …   **e** 21, 24, 29, 36, 45, …

2 For each of the sequences **a** to **e**
  i write down the next two terms   **ii** find the nth term.

  a 4, 10, 18, 28, …   **b** 15, 24, 35, 48, …   **c** 2, 6, 12, 20, …

  d 1, 3, 6, 10, …   **e** 6, 12, 20, 30, …

3 Look at each of the following sequences to see whether the rule is linear, quadratic on n^2 alone or fully quadratic. Then

  i write down the nth term   **ii** write down the 50th term.

  a 8, 13, 20, 29, …   **b** 8, 11, 14, 17, …   **c** 8, 15, 24, 35, …

  d 0, 5, 12, 21, 32, 45, …

★4 The picture shows a pattern of cards.

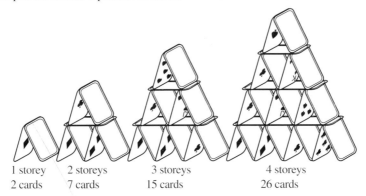

1 storey   2 storeys   3 storeys   4 storeys
2 cards   7 cards   15 cards   26 cards

a The four-storey house of cards is to be made into a five-storey house of cards. How many more cards are needed?

b Look at the sequence 2, 7, 15, 26, …

  i Calculate the sixth term in this sequence.

  ii Explain how you found your answer.

Chapter 25   Graphs 3

HOMEWORK 25A

1 a Copy and complete the table to draw the graph of $y = 2x^2$ for $-3 \leq x \leq 3$.

x	−3	−2	−1	0	1	2	3
$y = 2x^2$	18		2			8	

b Use the graph to find the value of y when $x = -1.4$.

c Use the graph to find the values of x that give a y-value of 10.

2 a Copy and complete the table to draw the graph of $y = x^2 + 3$ for $-5 \leq x \leq 5$.

x	−5	−4	−3	−2	−1	0	1	2	3	4	5
$y = x^2 + 3$	28		12					7			28

b Use the graph to find the value of y when $x = 2.5$.

c Use the graph to find the values of x that give a y-value of 10.

★3 a Copy and complete the table to draw the graph of $y = x^2 - 3x + 2$ for $-3 \leq x \leq 4$.

x	−3	−2	−1	0	1	2	3	4
$y = x^2 - 3x + 2$	20			2			2	

b Use the graph to find the value of y when $x = -1.5$.

c Use the graph to find the values of x that give a y-value of 2.5.

1 **a** Copy and complete the table to draw the graph of $y = x^2 - 3x + 2$ for $-1 \le x \le 5$.

x	−1	0	1	2	3	4	5
$y = x^2 - 3x + 2$	6	2			1		

   b Use your graph to find the roots of the equation $x^2 - 3x + 2 = 0$

2 **a** Copy and complete the table to draw the graph of $y = x^2 - 5x + 4$ for $-1 \le x \le 6$.

x	−1	0	1	2	3	4	5	6
$y = x^2 - 5x + 4$	10	4				0		

   b Use your graph to find the roots of the equation $x^2 - 5x + 4 = 0$

3 **a** Copy and complete the table to draw the graph of $y = x^2 + 4x - 6$ for $-5 \le x \le 2$.

x	−5	−4	−3	−2	−1	0	1	2
$y = x^2 + 4x - 6$	−1							6

   b Use your graph to find the roots of the equation $x^2 + 4x - 6 = 0$

1 **a** Complete the table to draw the graph of $y = \dfrac{12}{x}$ for $-12 \le x \le 12$.

x	−12	−6	−4	−3	−2	−1	1	2	3	4	6	12
$y = \dfrac{12}{x}$	−1			−4					4			1

   b Use your graph to find
   i the y-value when $x = 1.5$ **ii** the x-value when $y = 5.5$

★**2** **a** Complete the table to draw the graph of $y = \dfrac{8}{x}$ for $-8 \le x \le 8$.

x	−8	−5	−4	−2	−1	1	2	4	5	8
$y = \dfrac{8}{x}$										

   b Use your graph to find
   i the y-value when $x = 3.5$ **ii** the x-value when $y = 5$

3 **a** Complete the table to draw the graph of $y = \dfrac{50}{x}$ for $0 \le x \le 50$.

x	1	2	5	10	25	50
$y = \dfrac{50}{x}$						

   b On the same axes, draw the line $y = x + 30$.
   c Use your graph to find the x-values of the points where the graphs cross.

1 **a** Complete the table to draw the graph of $y = x^3 + 1$ for $-3 \le x \le 3$.

x	-3	-2	-1	0	1	2	3
$y = x^3 + 1$	-26			1			28

   b Use your graph to find the y-value for an x-value of 1.2.

★2 **a** Complete the table to draw the graph of $y = x^3 + 2x$ for $-2 \le x \le 3$.

x	-2	-1	0	1	2	3
$y = x^3 + 2x$	-12		0		12	

   b Use your graph to find the y-value for an x-value of 2.5.

3 **a** Draw the graph of $y = x^3 - x^2$ for $-3 \le x \le 3$.
   b Use your graph to find the y-value for an x-value of 1.8.

Chapter 26   Dimensional analysis

Find an expression for the perimeter of each of these shapes.

1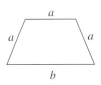

2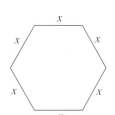

3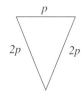

4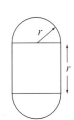

5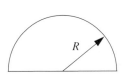

6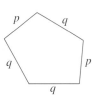

★7 The diagram shows a child's play brick in the shape of a prism.
The following formulae represent certain quantities connected with this prism.
$$\pi ab \quad \pi(a + b) \quad \pi abl \quad \pi(a + b)l$$
Which of the formulae represents a length?

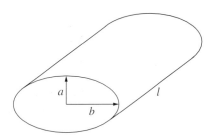

Find a formula for each of these areas.

1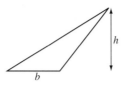

2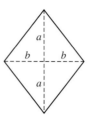

3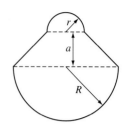

4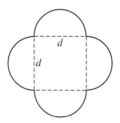

5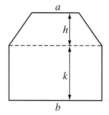

6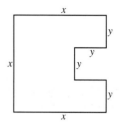

★**7** One of the formulae in the list below can be used to calculate the area of material in a lampshade. Which formula is it?

   a $\pi h(a + b)^2$ **b** $\pi h^2(a + b)$ **c** $\pi h(a + b)$ **d** $\pi h^2(a + b)^2$

Find a formula for each of these volumes.

1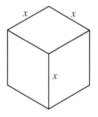

2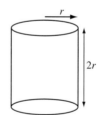

3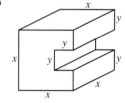

4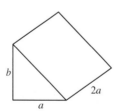

5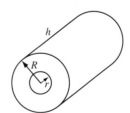

6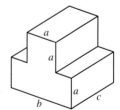

★7 The dimensions of four cuboids are shown.

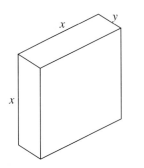 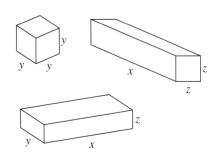

The expressions x^2y, xz and $2(x + y)$ give the perimeter of a face of one of the cuboids, or the area of a face of one of the cuboids, or the volume of one of the cuboids. Complete the statements below with the word perimeter, area or volume.

a x^2y gives a ......   **b** $2(x + y)$ gives a ......   **c** xz gives an ....

HOMEWORK 26D

1   Indicate by L, A, V or [L], [L²], [L³] whether the following quantities are lengths, areas or volumes, or none of these (N).

a   1 yard

b   12 hectares

c   Paint in a can

d   Weight of this book

e   Thickness of this book

f   Amount of paper used to print this book

g   110 decibels

h   Amount of water flowing from a tap

i   Latitude and longitude

j $m\,s^{-2}$

2   Each of these represents a length, an area or a volume. Indicate by writing L, A or V which it is.

a $ab + cd$ **b** $a^2b + c^2d$ **c** $ab(c + d)$ **d** $\frac{4}{3}\pi r^3$

e $\pi r^2 + 2\pi rh$ **f** $\frac{2}{3}\pi r^3 + \pi r^2h$ **g** $\frac{ab + cb}{b}$ **h** $\frac{a^3b + b^3a}{c}$

★3   This diagram shows the cross-section of a barn. A farmer wants to estimate the area of a cross-section of a warehouse.

a   Explain why the formula

$$A = \frac{H + 2W + L}{5}$$

cannot be a suitable formula for him to use.

b   Look at these formulae.

i $A = \frac{4WHL}{5}$ **ii** $A = \frac{L(4H + 2W)}{5}$ **iii** $A = \frac{LW + 4H}{5}$

One of these formulae can be used to estimate the area of the cross-section. Which is it? Give a reason for your answer.

HOMEWORK 26E

1   Indicate whether each of these formulae is consistent (C) or inconsistent (I).

a $a^2 + cd$ **b** $a^2b + cb$ **c** $ab(c^2 + d)$ **d** $r^2 + \frac{4}{3}\pi r$

e $\frac{2}{3}\pi r^3 + 2\pi rh$ **f** $\pi(a^3 + b^3)$ **g** $(a^2 + b)(a + b^2)$ **h** $(x + y)(x - y)$

2 **i** Write down whether each formula is consistent (C) or inconsistent (I).

    ii When it is consistent, say whether it represents a length (L), an area (A) or a volume (V).

    a $\pi a^2 + cd$ **b** $\dfrac{\pi(ab + cd)}{a}$ **c** $\pi r^2 h + 2\pi r$ **d** $(\pi + 2)a$

    e $abc + bca + cab$ **f** $\dfrac{\pi ab + \pi r^3}{a}$ **g** $a(b + c) + \pi r^2$ **h** $\dfrac{\pi(a^2 + b^2)}{c^2}$

3 What power * would make each formula consistent?

    a $\pi r^* h + \frac{4}{3}\pi r^3$ **b** $\dfrac{a^* b + r^2}{c}$ **c** $\pi a^2(b^* + ab)$ **d** $2a^* b + \pi r^3$

★4 In the following formulae r and h represent a length. For each formula, state whether it represents a length, an area, a volume or none of them.

    a $2\pi r^2 h$ **b** $\pi r^2(r + h)$ **c** $\sqrt{r^2 + h^2}$ **d** $\dfrac{r^2}{2\pi h}$ **e** $3\pi + r$

Chapter 27   Proof

HOMEWORK 27A

1 If m and n are integers then $(m^2 - n^2)$, $2mn$ and $(m^2 + n^2)$ will form three sides of a right-angled triangle. e.g. Let $m = 5$ and $n = 3$, $m^2 - n^2 = 16$, $2mn = 30$, $m^2 + n^2 = 34$ and $34^2 = 1156$, $16^2 + 30^2 = 256 + 900 = 1156$ Prove this result.

2 Explain why the triangle number sequence 1, 3, 6, 10, 15, 21, 28, … follows the pattern of two odd numbers followed by two even numbers.

3 $10p + q$ is a multiple of 7. Prove that $3p + q$ is also a multiple of 7.

4 ABCD is a trapezium. The diagonals DB and AC meet at E. Prove that the triangles ADE and BCE are equal in area.

5 ABCD is a rectangle. CEF is a triangle congruent to triangle ACD. BCE is a straight line. The line AC is extended to meet EF at P. Prove that AP is perpendicular to EF.

6 An isosceles trapezium is cut along a diagonal and the pieces put together as shown.

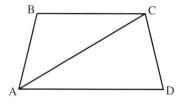 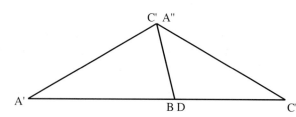

    a Prove that A′BC″ is a straight line.
    b Prove that the triangle is isosceles.
    c Explain why the triangle formed could never be equilateral.

7 Prove that the square of the sum of two consecutive integers minus the sum of the squares of the two integers is four times a triangular number.
    e.g. Let the two integers be 6 and 7. $(6 + 7)^2 - (6^2 + 7^2) = 169 - 85 = 84 = 4 \times 21$

8 Take any 4 numbers from the Fibonacci sequence, for example 8, 13, 21, 34. Prove that the following results are true.

    a The sum of the first and fourth terms is double the third.

       e.g. $34 + 8 = 42 = 2 \times 21$

    b The difference between the first and fourth terms is double the second term.

       e.g. $34 - 8 = 26 = 2 \times 13$

    c The difference between the squares of the second and third terms is equal to the product of the first and fourth terms.

       e.g. $21^2 - 13^2 = 272 = 8 \times 34$

9 a, b, c, d are consecutive integers. Prove that $bd - ac$ is always odd.

HOMEWORK 27B

1 **a** Show that $2(5(x - 2) + y) = 10(x - 1) + 2y - 10$

    b Prove that this trick works:

       Think of two numbers less than 10.

       Subtract 2 from the larger number and then multiply by 5.

       Add the smaller number and multiply by 2.

       Add 9 and subtract the smaller number.

       Add 1 to both the tens digits and the units digits to obtain the numbers first thought of

    c Prove why the following trick works.

       Choose two numbers. One with one digit the other with 2 digits.

       Subtract 9 times the first number from 10 times the second number.

       The units digit of the answer is the single digit number chosen and the sum of the other digits plus the units digit is the other number chosen.

       e.g. Choose 7 and 23. $(23 \times 10) - (7 \times 9) = 167$.

       The single digit number chosen is 7 the two digits number chosen is $16 + 7 = 23$.

2 a, b, c and d are four consecutive integers. Prove that

    a $bc - ad = 2$ **b** $ab + bc + cd + da + 1$ is a square number.

3 Prove that $(3n - 1)^2 + (3n)^2 + (3n + 1)^2 = (5n)^2 + (n - 1)^2 + (n + 1)^2$

4 Prove that $(n - 1)^2 + n^2 + (n + 1)^2 = 3n^2 + 2$

HOMEWORK 27C

1 **a** What is the nth term of the sequence 1, 4, 7, 10, 13, 16, ...

    b Explain why there is no multiple of 3 in the sequence.

    c Prove that the sum of any 5 consecutive numbers in the sequence is a multiple of 5.

2 This question was first set in an examination in 1929.

    $10^x = \dfrac{a}{b}, \quad 10^y = \dfrac{b}{a}$, Prove that $x + y = 0$

3 Two circles touch externally at T. A line ATB is drawn through T. The common tangent at T and the tangents at A and B meet at P and Q. prove that PB is parallel to AQ.

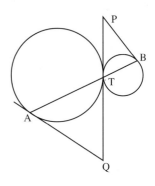

4 *m* and *n* are integers. Explain why
  a the product $n(n + 1)$ must be even   **b** $2m + 1$ is always an odd number.
  c Look at the following numbers pattern

$$1^2 - 1 = \mathbf{0}$$
$$2^2 - 1 = 3$$
$$3^2 - 1 = \mathbf{8}$$
$$4^2 - 1 = 15$$
$$5^2 - 1 = \mathbf{24}$$
$$6^2 - 1 = 35$$

  i Extend the pattern for 5 more lines to show that alternate values are multiples of 8.
  ii Prove that this is true.

5 a Prove that the angles subtended by the chord at the circumference of a circle are equal.
  b PQRS is a cyclic quadrilateral. PR and QS meet at T. Angles x, $2x$, $3x$ and $5x$ are marked on the diagram.
  i Find x.
  ii Show that the angles of the quadrilateral and angle STP form a number sequence.

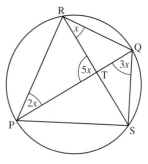

6 p, q and r are three consecutive numbers. Prove that $pq = r^2$.

7 ACB and ADB are right-angled triangles. The lengths are as marked.
  a Use Pythagoras' theorem to show that $x^2 = r^2 + s^2$.
  b Use Pythagoras' theorem on both triangles ACB and ADB to prove that $xt = sy$.

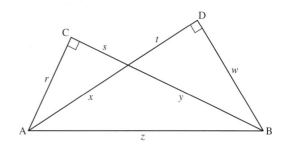